BRIDGES OF THE WORLD

AN ILLUSTRATED HISTORY

TIM & ANNE LOCKE

Introduction by Eric DeLony

CONTENTS

Written by Tim & Anne Locke
Introduction by Eric DeLony

Introduction supplied and used with permission of the International
Council on Monuments and Sites (ICOMOS) and The International Committee
for the Conservation of the Industrial Heritage (TICCIH), first published in the
ICOMOS-TICCIH joint Thematic Study
'Context for World Heritage Bridges'
© 1996 ICOMOS and TICCIH

International Council on
Monuments and Sites
Conseil International
des Monuments et des Sites

Foreword and conclusion of introduction by Eric DeLony

© 2008 Automobile Association Developments Ltd 2008

Managing Editor: David Popey
Senior Art Editor: Nick Otway
Picture Researcher: Vivien Little
Image Retouching and Internal Repro: Sarah Montgomery & Michael Moody
Verifier: Russ Swan
Proofreader: Barry Gage
Indexer: Marie Lorimer
Production: Rachel Davis

Maps created by the Mapping Services Department of AA Publishing
Relief Map Images supplied by Mountain High Maps®
Copyright © 1993 Digital Wisdom Inc.

Produced by AA Publishing Visit the AA at www.theAA.com/travel
Copyright © Automobile Association Developments Limited 2008

ISBN: 978-0-7495-5911-3

Published by AA Publishing (a trading name of Automobile Association Developments
Limited, whose registered office is Fanum House, Basing View, Basingstoke, Hampshire
RG21 4EA; registered number 1878835).

A03796

Colour separation by Mullis Morgan Group Ltd
Printed in China by Leo Paper

CONTENTS

FOREWORD

Eric DeLony,
Chief (Retired), Historic American Engineering Record (HAER), US National Park Service

Most people perceive bridges as engineered objects, sometimes inspiring and beautiful but more likely as a utilitarian part of our transport network. However, like most of the bridges featured in *Bridges of the World*, the first crossing detailed here is anything but ordinary. First opened in 1566, Stari Most was almost entirely reconstructed in 2004 following its destruction during conflict in the former Yugoslavia in 1993. The replicated bridge has since become a symbol of reconciliation, international cooperation and of the peaceful coexistence of diverse cultural, ethnic and religious communities. Through the help of an international scientific committee, the reconstructed bridge and surrounding restored community has been designated a World Heritage Site by UNESCO.

Many bridges have come to embody the spirit and character of a place such as the Brooklyn Bridge does for New York or Tower Bridge for London. Indeed, the same can be said for different types of bridge. Ask any person about historic bridges and the first type that comes to mind are stone-arch spans for Europe and covered wooden spans for the USA. Few engineered structures – indeed, few historic structures of any type – captivate the imagination like bridges. They are the subject of countless books, poems, photographs and paintings, and they often serve as the backdrop of feature films. Romance and nostalgia, however, often masks the substantial engineering achievement that bridges represent. It is precisely this embodiment of both the cultural and the technological that give bridges their widespread appeal and understated significance.

Monumental or ordinary, for the last decade, it has been my aim to expand people's consciousness to think of bridges within their contexts – the countryside, highway or byway, scenic, urban or rural landscape. Viewed in this larger context, bridges become part of the social and cultural landscape, maintaining a scale and quality to the countryside or urban cityscape that is seldom duplicated by a modern concrete or steel girder span.

One also should think in terms of families or groups of bridges. Citizens, engineers and historians should think in terms of city bridges or families of bridges found in London, Paris, Prague, St. Petersburg, Pittsburgh, Los Angeles, Cleveland or Chicago. There are outstanding bridge cities and bridge families all over the world.

Sustainability – one of the major themes in today's engineering, architectural and construction worlds – is another argument that can be used to promote appreciation and preservation of historic bridges. When a community chooses to rehabilitate rather than replace any bridge, they exercise safety and efficiency while at the same time saving the structure for posterity and maintaining its associated street or landscape. Historic bridges can represent an engineering superlative and aesthetic marvel that deserves wider exposure. Others view bridges as metaphors symbolic of an emotional junction or, perhaps more traditionally, as a way of surmounting an obstacle.

It is likely to be in developing countries where hitherto undiscovered historic bridges will be found and new bridges built. Here will be the bridge finds and new bridges of the 21st century. For the developed world, we've used up the capacity bequeathed to us by previous generations, so one of our main issues is rehabilitating an aging infrastructure. Hopefully, the sustainability and cultural values of historic bridges will be part of this complex equation.

Bridges of the World features all kinds and types of bridges, ranging from the ancient to the contemporary, found on six continents and representing all the common building materials – wood, stone, iron, steel and concrete. Indeed the primary types are all covered – beam, arch, truss, movable, suspension and cable-stayed, the latter being the signature bridge type built throughout the world today.

So, for whom is this book written? Engineers, engineering educators, historians and academics will be interested because of the global coverage and superb imagery. Even though the structures featured in *Bridges of the World* will be familiar to most people, it is hoped that their relatively unknown individual stories will provide a fascinating introduction to anyone interested in architecture and the built environment. I hope that it will be of most interest to the ordinary citizen and enthusiast, because it is these people who will play a significant role in sustaining the world's outstanding bridges – both old and new.

7

BRIDGE BUILDING: AN ILLUSTRATED HISTORY

BRIDGE BUILDING: AN ILLUSTRATED HISTORY

Eric DeLony

INTRODUCTION

Bridging rivers, gorges, narrows, straits and valleys always has played an important role in the history of human settlement. Since ancient times, bridges, above all structures, have been the most visible testimony of the noble craft of engineering. A bridge can be defined in many ways, but Andrea Palladio, the great 16th-century Italian architect and engineer, probably came closest to the essence of bridge building when he said '...bridges should befit the spirit of the community by exhibiting commodiousness, firmness and delight'. In more practical terms, he went on to explain that the way to avoid having the bridge carried away by the violence of water was to construct the bridge without fixing any posts in the water. The goal of bridge builders and engineers has always been to follow Palladio's advice and create as wide a span as possible that is commodious, firm and occasionally delightful. Spanning greater distances is a distinct measure of engineering prowess and almost every year a new bridge stakes claim to breaking – whether its length, height, span or the greatest of its own particular field.

In terms of engineering, bridges are always discussed by design or type (beam, arch, truss, cantilever, suspension, or movable); length (usually expressed in terms of clear or overall span); and materials (stone, wood, cast and wrought iron and what we use today – concrete and steel). One of the purposes of *Bridges of the World* is to provide a detailed look at significant structures around the world that best illustrate the history of bridge building.

WORLD HERITAGE SITES AND PRESERVATION

Much of our knowledge about bridge engineering would be incomplete without the preservation of those structures that have broken boundaries through sheer ingenuity, invention and engineering prowess. It is here that the criteria of the World Heritage Committee becomes useful when it comes to the terminology of how we should appreciate bridge structures around the world

The World Heritage Committee states that to be of World Heritage status a monument or site must be of outstanding universal value. It must illustrate or interpret the heritage of the world in terms of engineering, technology, transportation, communication, industry, history, or culture. World Heritage industrial sites and monuments must be 'irreplaceable sources of life and inspiration'.

In representing a masterpiece of human creative genius, a heritage site must have exerted great influence, over a span of time or within a cultural area of the world, on developments in engineering theory, technology, construction, transportation and communication. They must be an outstanding example of a type which illustrates a significant stage in bridge engineering or technological developments.

Previous page The Ponte dei Salti, meaning 'bridge of the jumps', at Lavertezzo in Switzerland is also known as the Roman Bridge for its typical Roman construction. However, the bridge actually dates from the 17th century.

Right The large granite slabs of the Tarr Steps in Exmoor National Park (UK) were, according to local legend, placed by the devil to win a bet. The prehistoric bridge is thought to date from 1000 BC.

Above The Natural Bridge is a stone arch of limestone standing above Cedar Creek in the Shenandoah Valley of Virginia. Once part of the roof of a large cavern, it is crossed by US Highway 11.

THE THREE ESSENTIAL TYPES

The first bridges were natural, such as the huge rock arch that spans the Ardèche in France, or Natural Bridge in Virginia, in the United States. The first human-made bridges were tree trunks laid across streams in girder fashion, flat stones, such as the clapper bridges of Dartmoor in Devon in the United Kingdom (see pages 112-115), or festoons of vegetation, twisted or braided and hung in suspension. These examples are essentially three types – beam, arch and suspension. They have been known and built since ancient times and are the origins from which engineers and builders derived various combinations such as the truss, cantilever, cable-stayed, tied-arch and movable spans.

LIVE AND DEAD LOAD

The essential difference among types is the way they bear their own weight known as – the 'dead load' and the 'live load' – a person, the railway train, wind, or snow that is applied to the bridge. The weight of beam, truss and girder bridges bears directly downwards from their ends on the ground, piers, or abutments. Arch bridges thrust outwards as well as downwards, acting in compression. The cables of suspension bridges act in tension, pulling inwards against their anchorages. If two or more beam or girder spans are joined together over piers, they become continuous, a form favoured by European engineers, who had the mathematical knowledge to analyse previously indeterminate stresses.

A more complex form of the beam is the truss, a rigid, self-supporting system of triangles transferring both dead and live loads to the abutments or piers. A more complex form of the girder is the cantilever, where trussed and anchored ends of the girder support a central span. They were favoured for deep gorges or wide fast-flowing streams where falsework, a temporary structure, usually of timber, erected to assist in the construction of the permanent bridge, is impossible to build.

Above The Pont d'Arc in the Rhone-Alps region of Southern France is a natural limestone arch formed over thousands of years by the action of the River Ardéche that runs beneath.

The three principal types – beam, arch and suspension – often were combined in a variety of ways to form composite structures, with the type being selected depending on the nature of the crossing, the span required, the materials at hand, and the type of load anticipated – pedestrian, vehicular, railroad, or a channel of water as in aqueducts.

PRIMITIVE BRIDGES

Other than the clapper bridges found in parts of the UK and similar spans surviving in other countries, bridges dating from prehistoric periods are rare. Bridges of twisted vines and creepers found in India, Africa and South America, the ancient cantilevers of China, Kashmir and Japan (if any survive) or the wooden arches of Japan show primitive ingenuity and craft technology, even if their materials are not original.

In 51BC, during the Gallic War, Caesar attested to the construction of narrow wooden bridges by Gallic builders over wide rivers as the Loire, Seine and Allier of 200m (600ft) span, used by pedestrians and domestic animals. The stone vault probably first sprang forth in Anatolia and the Aegean region of Asia Minor (central and western Turkey) in the 2nd millennium BC for short spans in civic construction. The Mesopotamian civilizations introduced the first major development of brick vaulting in the royal palaces, and also probably the first important arch bridges in the 6th century BC.

ROMAN BRIDGES

The greatest bridge builders of antiquity were the Romans. They applied a civil engineering repertoire on an unprecedented grand scale and achieved impressive results. Roman engineering introduced four significant developments to the art of bridge building that never had been prominent before: the discovery and extensive use of natural cement, development of the coffer dam, perfection and widespread application of the semi-circular masonry arch.

Above The clapper bridge at Scorhill may be one of the smallest in the Exmoor National Park (UK). Still in use, its single pillar and two-slab construction provides a useful crossing of the River North Teign.

Left The Aqueduct of Segovia, Spain, is an extremely well-preserved piece of Roman infrastructure and follows construction principles set out by Vitruvius in his *De Architecura* published in the 1st century.

13

Above A surviving arch at the entrance to the site of the amphitheatre at the ancient Roman town of Rusellae in Etruria (Tuscany, Italy). The settlement was abandoned in the Middle Ages.

Above The Zhaozhou Bridge, China, has survived numerous earthquakes and at least eight wars during its 1500-year history. Located in Hebei Province, it is also known as the Safe Crossing Bridge.

In these important respects, the Roman engineer vastly improved upon the efforts of their predecessors. Public water supply was the most significant aspect of Roman civil engineering: nothing like it had been achieved before nor was it to be emulated until the 19th century. Structural evolution achieved by Roman engineers is manifest in aqueducts, dam construction and highway bridges that relied on the development of concrete, and a growing awareness of its strength.

The Romans mixed a cement, *pozzolana*, found near the Italian town of Pozzuoli (ancient Puteoli), with lime, sand and water to form a mortar that did not disintegrate when exposed to water. It was used as a binder in piers and arch spandrels and mass-formed in foundations. Coffer dams (temporary enclosures built in river beds to keep the water out while the foundations were established) were made by driving timber piles into the river bed, removing water from the area enclosed, and then excavating the soft ground inside. Despite the use of coffer dams, Roman bridge foundations typically were not deep enough to provide sufficient protection against the relentless scour. Most of the Roman bridges that survive are those built on solid rock such as the Pont du Gard aqueduct (cAD14, see pages 68-71) near Nîmes (France), the Alcantara Bridge (AD98, see pages 98-99) on the Spanish-Portuguese border, and the aqueduct at Segovia (AD98, see page 71), which are three of the most famous surviving Roman bridges and aqueducts.

BRIDGES OF ASIA
Although fewer structures survive, bridge building in Asia extends back earlier in time than in Europe; structural concepts of suspension, cantilever and arch were first developed there with great sophistication.

CHINESE BRIDGES
Following the decline of the Roman Empire with its many engineering achievements, beam, arch, suspension and cantilever bridge building flourished in China while languishing in Europe for nearly eight centuries. Chinese bridge builders experimented with forms and materials, perfecting their techniques.

In fact many bridge forms originated in China. Marco Polo told of 12,000 bridges built of wood, stone and iron near the ancient city of Kin-sai. The first chain-link suspension bridge, the Panhogiao or Panho Bridge (c206BC), was built by General Panceng during the Han Dynasty. In 1665, a missionary named Kircher described another chain-link suspension bridge of 61m (200ft) made up of 20 iron links, a common bridge type built during the Ming Dynasty that was not adapted until the 19th century in America and Europe. China's oldest surviving bridge, and the world's oldest open-spandrel segmental arch, is the Zhaozhou Bridge (cAD605), attributed to Li Chun and built south-west of Beijing in Hebei Province during the Song Dynasty. Its thin, curved stone slabs were joined with iron dovetails so that the arch could yield without collapsing. This technique allowed the bridge to adjust to the rise and fall of abutments bearing on spongy, plastic soils and the live loads of traffic.

JAPANESE BRIDGES
Picturesque bridges, such as the Kintai Bridge at Iwakuni (1673), with its five wooden arches intricately wedged, slotted and dovetailed together, are mainly found in Japan. The superstructure of the Kintai (see pages 190-193) has been constantly rebuilt and so maintaining the fine craft tradition of the bridge keepers for centuries. Shogun's Bridge (1638), crossing the Daiya-gawa River in the sacred City of Nikko, is the oldest known cantilever. The bridge was badly damaged in the typhoon of 1902, rebuilt, and exists today bearing foot traffic. It consists of hewn stone piers pierced with rectangular holes that permit the insertion of tightly fitting cut-stone struts, two anchor spans, timber beams jutting out in cantilever form and a suspended span.

Above The Pont du Gard, France, is probably the most famous aqueduct in the world. Remarkably, the three-tiered structure was built entirely without the use of mortar, with each stone cut to fit together precisely.

Right The remaining masonry of a Roman aqueduct, near Carthage; just a small part of one of the longest aqueducts ever built. Sections of it were still in use until the 17th century.

Above The Khaju Bridge in Iran, links the Khaju and Zoroastrian quarters of the city of Esfahan. Sluice gates under the archways regulate the water flow of the Zayandeah River for irrigation purposes.

Other fine bridges survive in Iran, such as the Bridge of Khaju at Esfahan (1667, see page 184), with 18 pointed arches, carrying an 26m (85ft) wide roadway with walled, shaded passageways, flanked by pavilions and watch towers. This magnificent bridge, combining architecture and engineering in splendid functional harmony, also served as a dam, and included a hostelry where travellers found cool rooms for rest and refreshment after hot desert crossings.

MEDIEVAL BRIDGES

The revival of bridge building in Europe following the fall of the Roman Empire was marked by the spread of the pointed arch westward from its origins in the Middle East. The pointed arch typically was a Gothic architectural form important structurally in the development of palaces, castles and especially the cathedrals of western Europe, but not very important for bridges. Medieval bridges continued such multi-functional traditions as the Esfahan Bridge in Iran. Chapels, shops, tollhouses and towers adorned fortified bridges such the 1355 Pont Valentré at Cahors (see pages 76–79) or the Monnow Bridge (1272, 1296) at Monmouth, Wales (see page 78), which were built with defensive ramparts, firing slits and drawspans.

Christian religious orders formed after the fall of the Roman Empire greatly assisted travellers by building bridges. In western and central Europe, religious groups managed popular financial institutions, with Papal sanction, both for bridge construction and for hospitals. The influence of these groups lasted from the end of the 12th to the early 14th century, and their perseverance ensured the construction of major bridges over wide rivers such as the Rhône and the Danube.

The bridge over the Rhône at Avignon in France (1187, see pages 72-75), for example, a wooden deck on stone piers, was built by such an order under the inspired vision of a young shepherd, later canonized as St Bénézet for his accomplishment. The four surviving arches, dating from the bridge's rebuilding around 1350, rank as one of the most remarkable monuments of medieval times in view of the 31–34m (101–110ft) elliptical arches with radii varying at the crown and haunches.

As the Middle Ages drew to a close, stone arches of remarkable spans were built in mountain valleys where rock abutments provided solid foundations for spans in excess of 50m (164ft), such as the Vieille-Brioude and the Grand Pont du Doux in France.

RENAISSANCE AND NEO-CLASSICAL BRIDGES

The great era of medieval bridge building was followed by a period known as *Quattrocento*, the transition from the medieval period to the Italian Renaissance, when the confidence and unbounded enterprise of engineers was manifested in bridges like the 1345 Ponte Vecchio, an early Florentine bridge in Italy, designed by Taddeo Gaddi (see pages 86-89) with its three segmental arches. This was followed by the technical efficiency and artistic advancement of Renaissance ideals of civic order during the Neo-Classical period of the 17th and 18th centuries, represented by long span and multiple stone arches: eg Santa Trinità (1569) in Florence, the Rialto (1591) in Venice (see pages 84-85) and the Pont Neuf (1607) in Paris (see pages 58-59). These bridges are among the most famous bridges in the world today. Renaissance engineers had learned much about foundations since Roman times, though they rarely were able to excavate deeply enough to reach hard strata. They had, however, perfected techniques of spread footings – wide timber grillages resting on piles driven into the river bed upon which stone piers were laid. In the foundation of the Rialto Bridge, designer Antonio da Ponte drove 6,000 timber piles, capped by three stepped grillages so that the abutment stones could be laid perpendicular to the thrust lines of the arch. Though built on soft alluvial soils, the bridge continues to support a street of jewellery shops enjoyed by tourists four centuries later.

Above The Pont Valentré, France, is a significant example of fortified architecture from the Middle Ages. Built between 1308 and 1378, the bridge was extensively restored in 1879.

Left The Kintai Bridge, Japan, spans the Nishiki River. Originally built in 1673, the structure has been constantly renewed and updated following destruction by war and fire throughout its lifetime.

Above The hump-backed Puente de Roman in Cangas de Onis, Spain, crosses the Sella River. However, the name is a misnomer as the bridge actually dates from the medieval period.

BRIDGE BUILDING

THE ADVENT OF THE NEO-CLASSICAL

The end of the Italian Renaissance witnessed a new vision of bridge construction. More than merely utilitarian, bridges were designed as elegant, grand passage-ways that were part of the visual perspective of the idealized cityscape – major accents to the totally redesigned merchant and capital cities. No country attempted to advance this concept more than France at the end of the 16th century, where a national transportation department of architects and engineers was set up, responsible for designing bridges and roads. This corps of specialists gave the Neo-Classical period a range of monumental and elegant bridges on rivers as the Loire (Blois, Orléans, Saumur) and the Seine in Paris. This model spread all over Europe, producing large monumental urban bridges in capitals such as London and Prague.

In Italy, Bartolomeo Ammannati evolved a new form for the Santa Trinità Bridge – a peculiar double-curved arch whose departure from an ellipse was deliberately concealed by a decorative escutcheon at the crown. Its 1:7 rise-to-span ratio resulted in an elegantly shallow, long-arch span widely adapted in other bridges of the Renaissance. The bridge was reconstructed using original stones recovered from the river following demolition during the Second World War.

THE FRENCH STYLE

By the mid-18th century, masonry bridge building had reached its apogee. French engineer Jean-Rodolphe Perronet designed and built the Pont de Neuilly (1774), the Pont de Saint-Maxence (1785) and the Pont de la Concorde (1791), the latter completed when the engineer was 83. Perronet's design goals were to slim down the piers and to stretch arches to the maximum. The Pont de la Concorde still represents the perfection of masonry arch construction, even though sceptical officials forced Perronet to shorten the unprecedented centre span of the bridge to 28m (92ft). Long, elegant, elliptical arches, piers half their former widths, special machinery for construction, and the introduction of an architectural motif used until the 1930s, the open parapet with turned balusters, completed this outstanding bridge. Widened in the 1950s, its original appearance was carefully maintained. Another masterpiece of the French Classical style is the Pont de Bordeaux of 19 arches, more than 500m (1,640ft), completed in 1822.

EARLY BRITISH EXPERTISE

In the United Kingdom, a young Swiss engineer, Charles Labelye, was building the English equivalent of Perronet's bridges. On his first bridge, Westminster (1750) over the Thames in London, he developed the caisson, which made it possible for pier foundations to be built in deep, fast-flowing waters. To solve a problem that had confounded bridge builders since Roman times, Labelye used huge timber boxes constructed on shore, floated into position, and slowly sunk to the bottom of the river by the weight of the masonry piers being laid above. Fifteen semicircular arches, incrementally diminishing in length from the centre and rising in a graceful camber, set a high engineering and architectural standard that stood without challenge for more than 100 years.

Britain's other great bridge designer during this period, John Rennie, built the first Waterloo Bridge in 1811. Its level road and arches lasted until 1938. Rennie's next great bridge was Southwark Bridge (1819), also over the Thames in London, which was built not in stone but in the new miracle material of the 19th century – cast iron. It had three arches whose central span of 73m (240ft) demonstrated the potential of the new material in a very dramatic way.

WOODEN BRIDGES

Wooden bridges can lay claim to be some of the most ancient structures in the world. The first Roman bridge, the Pons Sublicius (c621BC), was a wood-pile structure over the Tiber in Rome, extending pedestrian access to the Aventine Hill. The earliest detailed description of

Above The oldest of the three bridges across the Grand Canal in Venice, the Rialto Bridge is the latest, and last, in a series of structures that stood here from the 12th century onwards.

Above For many years the widest bridge in Paris, the Pont Neuf's structure has never been altered, and the original wooden pilings supporting the foundations are still in place beneath the surface of the Seine.

Right The Renaissance structure of the Ponte Santa Trinita (Italy) was built by the architect Bartolomeo Ammanati between 1567 and 1569. It is sited just downstream from its more famous neighbour, the Ponte Vecchio.

a wooden bridge, a timber-pile structure over the Rhine constructed in 55BC, was written by Julius Caesar in his *De Bello Gallico*. The best-surviving model of this type survives today over the Brenta at Bassano a Grappa, near Venice in Italy. It was built by Palladio in 1561, destroyed in 1945, and reconstructed identical to the original in 1948.

By the mid-18th century, carpenters working in the forested regions of the world further developed the timber truss bridge. The most famous examples were by two Swiss brothers, Johannes and Ulrich Grubenmann, who built bridges at Schaffhausen, Reichenau and Wettingen that combined diagonal struts and trusses to produce remarkably long spans for their time. The Schaffhausen Bridge (1757), over the Rhine in northern Switzerland, had two spans, 52m and 59m (171ft and 193ft) respectively, which rested lightly on an intermediate pier when loaded. It was burned by the French during the Napoleonic Wars in 1799. One of the few Grubenmann bridges to survive is Rumlangbrücke (1766), with a span of 27m (89ft).

NEW WORLD INSPIRATIONS

European engineers visiting the New World during the 19th century marvelled at the spans achieved by American timber bridges. Especially noteworthy was Louis Wernwag's 104m (340ft) arch truss of 1812, the 'Colossus' over the Schuylkill in Philadelphia, the longest spanning bridge in the world at the time. Covered bridges (see pages 214-217), sheathed in wood to keep the structural timbers from deteriorating, are an icon of the American landscape. Outstanding spans that survive today include the Cornish-Windsor Bridge (1866) over the Connecticut River and the Bridgeport Bridge (1862), whose clear span of 63m (208ft) makes this gateway to the California goldfields the second longest single span. It is estimated that some 750 wooden covered bridges survive in the USA, more than in any other country.

THE LESS EXPENSIVE ALTERNATIVE

Regardless of the capability of advanced societies like the Romans to build bridges in stone, the material for the ages, its expense always remained a problem. Wooden bridges were an economic alternative important to every civilisation during all historic periods from prehistoric times to the first American settlement, from classical Rome to the European Enlightenment, including China, Japan and southeast Asia. Wooden bridges have played a major role in the history of human development. The architectural varieties and structural types – girder, arch, suspension, truss, pontoon and covered – were numerous. By virtue of the nature of their material, extant examples are scarce, as is the historic record. Nature, acts of God, war and arson have decimated wooden bridges throughout history. In some cases the bridge has been replaced and a semblance of the original has been secured. However, further efforts are needed to identify, access and protect wooden structures of all kinds.

THE RENAISSANCE AND NEO-CLASSICAL: THEORETICAL ADVANCES

Thanks to Galileo, Renaissance mathematicians and scientists were able to understand beam action and the theory of framed structures. The truss, used by the Romans as stiffening on the Rhine bridge (55 BC) and in roof structures, was refined by the Italian architect-engineer Andrea Palladio. His classic treatise on Greek and Roman architecture, *I Quattro Libri dell'Architettura*, was published in 1570, and was widely distributed after translation into English by Isaac Ware in 1755. It contained the first drawings of a truss, the simplest and most easily visualized form for transferring both dead and live loads to piers and abutments, accomplished by a rigid self-supporting system of triangles. Palladio built several truss bridges, the most important being the Bassano Bridge (1561) over the River Brenta in the Veneto region in northern Italy. Destroyed twice, it has been carefully rebuilt, faithfully following the original layout and exists today as the only example of one of Palladio's bridges. The truss form, derived from the Romans, represents one of the Renaissance's most significant contributions to bridge building.

Above The Mathematical Bridge at Cambridge University (UK) owes much to knowledge introduced by the master carpenter William Etheridge, who had previously worked on the first Westminster Bridge across the River Thames.

Left Andrea Palladio's wooden covered bridge at Bassano del Grappa, Italy, has been rebuilt twice after being destroyed by flooding in 1748 and 1966. Each time, Palladio's layout and design has been retained.

Above Lucerne's Kapellbrücke (Chapel Bridge) of 1333 spans the River Reuss in Switzerland. The bridge is a popular tourist site, in part due to the gable paintings that run the length of the structure.

BRIDGE BUILDING

TREATISE, STUDY AND POLICY

Besides the truss form, Renaissance engineers also devised daring innovation in arch forms – the segmental, elliptical and multi-centred. The Hungarian, Janos Veranscics, reviewed these and other achievements in the structural arts at the end of the Renaissance in *Machinae Novae*, published in 1617. Several concepts that later became standard bridge practice first were illustrated in this volume: the tied arch, the Pauli or lenticular truss (in wood), the all-metal truss (in cast brass), a portable, metal chain-link suspension bridge, the use of metal in reinforcing wooden bridges and the eye-bar tension member (again created in brass).

In 1716, Henri Gautier published *Traité des Ponts*, the first treatise devoted entirely to bridge building, during the Age of Reason when empirical bridge design gave way to rationalism and scientific analysis. The book became a standard work of reference throughout the 18th century. It covered both timber and masonry bridges, their foundations, piers and centring.

A far-sighted policy that led to the first national department of transportation in France was started by Henri IV and Sully at the end of the 16th century. During the second half of the 17th century, it was reorganized by Colbert as the Corps des Ingénieurs des Ponts et Chaussées, a group of state architects and engineers, during the reign of Louis XIV. In 1747, the École des Ponts et Chaussées, the oldest academic institution in the world for civil engineering education in the design of roads and bridges, was started, with Perronet as its first director. The first theoretical studies concerning the stability of arches, transmission of forces and the multi-radius form were conducted at the school.

IRON BRIDGES

Though extremely versatile, wood has one obvious disadvantage – it burns. Wernwag's Colossus, destroyed by fire in 1838, is but one example of many outstanding wooden bridges lost in this manner throughout history. There was another material, however, whose use at the end of the 18th century offered bridge engineers an alternative to the traditional materials of timber, stone and brick. Although it had first been used in antiquity, iron was the miracle material of the Industrial Revolution. The Greeks and Romans had used it to reinforce stone pediments and columns in their temples and iron links had been forged by the Chinese and used in suspension bridges.

The successful smelting of iron with coke, rather than charcoal, by English ironmaster Abraham Darby in 1709 freed iron production from fuel shortage restrictions, made large castings possible, and facilitated creation of the arch ribs for the world's first iron bridge, built 70 years later (see pages 120-123). In 1754, Henry Cort of Southampton built the first rolling mill, making possible the efficient shaping of bar iron; in 1784 he patented a puddling furnace by means of which the carbon content in cast iron could be reduced to produce malleable iron. These two milestones of metallurgy realised the potential of iron as a major building material. Bridges were one of the first structural uses of iron, preceded only by columns (not yet beams) to support the floors of textile mills.

The first successful all-iron bridge in the world was designed by Thomas Farnolls Pritchard, an architect who suggested using the material as early as 1773. Built by two ironmasters, Abraham Darby and John Wilkinson, to demonstrate the versatility of cast iron, the bridge spans 30m (100ft) over the River Severn at Coalbrookdale (UK), on five semi-circular ribs of cast iron. The Iron Bridge was followed by a succession of cast-iron arches built throughout Europe. Few cast-iron arch bridges were built in the USA as the iron truss, derived from wooden forms, was preferred. However, the oldest iron arch in the US merits mention; Dunlaps Creek Bridge (1839), designed by Captain Richard Delafield of the Army Corps of Engineers for the National Road in Brownsville, Pennsylvania, survives to this day, still carrying traffic. Because the material could be moulded into elaborate shapes, extravagantly

Above The first of its kind, the Iron Bridge across the River Severn was raised in the summer of 1779. The bridge was permitted by an Act of Parliament and Abraham Darby III commissioned to cast and build the bridge.

Below Built in 1862, the Bow Bridge is a cast-iron structure in Central Park, New York. Designed by Calvert Vaux and Jacob Wrey Mould, the 18.3m (60ft) bridge crosses the Park's lake at its narrowest point.

22

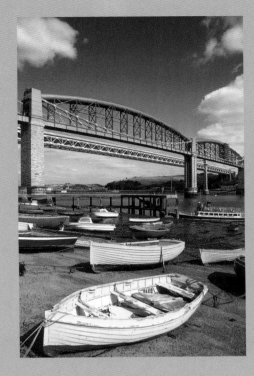

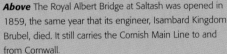

Left The current incarnation of the Rochester Bridge (Kent, UK) was built in 1914 after an inspection of the cast iron structure of 1856 revealed fractured ribs, the result of several boat collisions.

Above The Royal Albert Bridge at Saltash was opened in 1859, the same year that its engineer, Isambard Kingdom Brubel, died. It still carries the Cornish Main Line to and from Cornwall.

decorative iron arches were used for pedestrian bridges on the grounds of estates and imperial palaces, such as Catherine the Great's Tsarskoye Selo in St. Petersburg (Russia), or urban pleasure grounds, such as Central Park in New York City (USA). Both places have remarkable collections of cast-iron arch bridges.

ADVANCES IN ENGINEERING AND TECHNOLOGY

Engineers in the 19th century improved the technology of sinking foundations to bedrock. Up until that time, coffer dams and crude caissons were the only means by which foundations could be constructed in water. Their use was limited by the length of wooden piles and by soils that were unsuitable for pile driving because they were either too soft or too hard. Credit for developing the first pneumatic caisson belongs to William Cubitt and John Wright, who used the technique on the bridge (1851) over the River Medway at Rochester. It was similar to the caisson developed by Labelye, but differed in that the chamber resting on the river's bottom was airtight and required workmen to enter by means of airlocks after the water had been driven out by pneumatic pressure. Working in this environment, men suffered from the little understood 'caissons disease', now better known as 'the bends'. The eventual diagnosis of this condition permitted the construction of bridges of unprecedented scale, overcoming the impediment of deep, broad rivers. Isambard Kingdom Brunel used the technique for sinking the piers of his bridge at Chepstow, Wales and, on a much grander scale, on the Royal Albert Bridge (1859) over the Tamar at Saltash in Cornwall (UK, see pages 132-133). Here, the central pier was built on a wrought-iron caisson 11m (37ft) in diameter, sunk to bedrock in 21m (70ft) of water and 5m (16ft) of mud.

Another improvement in foundations in the early 19th century involved hydraulic cement. A better scientific understanding of the material by the Frenchman Louis Vicat and the Englishman Joseph Aspdin and discovery of the material in a natural state in 1796 on the Isle of Sheppey in the Thames estuary, by Lafarge at Le Teil (France) and by Canvass White on the Erie Canal in New York in 1818, led to its use in sinking foundations by the new method

23

BRIDGE BUILDING

of direct flow into coffer dams underwater, as at the suspension bridge at Tournon (France) in 1824. Hydraulic cement had the amazing ability to set under water, and was consequently used in aqueducts, piers and abutments, culverts and locks.

AFTER IRON BRIDGE

Following the construction of the Iron Bridge at Coalbrookdale, Thomas Telford, a gifted, self-educated Scottish engineer, built a number of cast-iron arches throughout Britain. These included canal aqueducts, which were extraordinarily innovative arrangements in which the cast iron had real structural value. On both the Longdon-on-Tern (1796) and the Pontcysyllte (1805) aqueducts, the cast-iron sections that formed the side walls of the trunk were wedge-shaped, behaving like the voussoirs (wedge-shaped stones) of a stone-arch bridge and bolted through flanges. Telford's most ambitious notion, however, was his proposal of 1800 for a single cast-iron arch of 183m (600ft) span over the Thames to replace Old London Bridge. An earlier proposal was unveiled in France by Montpetit in 1779 for a bridge of 122m (400ft) over the Seine, thought to have been the inspiration for Telford's idea. Even the young United States got into the act when Thomas Paine, the political philosopher, proposed an iron arch of 400ft span over the Schuylkill in Philadelphia. But the next most outstanding achievement after Coalbrookdale was the cast-iron arch over the River Wear at Sunderland, mainly because it actually was constructed. Completed in 1796 by Thomas Wilson, the bridge had an unprecedented span of 75m (246ft).

Above Thomas Wilson's Wearmouth Bridge was opened in 1796, the second British iron bridge after the famous Iron Bridge itself. It was reconstucted by Robert Stephenson in 1857. An 1879 rail bridge was built nearby.

Today, several collections of cast-iron arches survive in different countries, the largest being in the UK, six in the USA, a few in France and Spain, and a remarkable selection surviving in Russia, dating back to the reign of Catherine the Great.

COMPOSITE MATERIALS: DIFFERENT WAYS OF WORKING

By 1800, most European engineers were open to using cast iron. Architects, however, preferred traditional materials such as granite and marble for the visible parts of buildings and wood for hidden structural parts like roof trusses, and did not accept cast iron as having aesthetic merit or structural value. In the USA, still blessed with abundant virgin forests, the early 19th century was the era of 'carpenter engineers'. Men like Timothy Palmer, Lewis Wernwag, Theodore Burr, and Ithiel Town followed British custom by conceiving and building truss forms predicated on intuition and pragmatic rules of thumb. Their craft tradition of knowledge, passed down from master to apprentice, contrasted with the scientific analysis and mathematical formulas practised by French governmental engineers. Models were built and loaded to failure and broken members replaced with stronger ones until the model supported loadings equivalent to a real live load plus an all-important safety factor.

Patents were granted in the USA for composite wood and iron bridges, transitional structures that capitalized on the availability of cheap timber. When the American iron industry caught up with that of Europe by the mid 19th century, bridge building took the direction of composite pin-connected trusses, with sophisticated castings for joint blocks and compression members, and forged eyebars and wrought-iron rods for tension members, all fabricated to high tolerances. This allowed them to be assembled easily and inexpensively in the field by unskilled labour using simple tools and erection techniques. The system prevailed in the United States because the country lacked a skilled labour force, and the remoteness of many bridge sites hampered the use of sophisticated machinery or the shipping of large bridge parts over long distances. A spirited debate ensued between Britain and its former colony during the last quarter of the 19th century over which system was best: easily erected pin-connected trusses on the 'American plan', or European-style riveted trusses. Even though the rigid riveted truss was of superior design, American bridges remained competitive in world bridge markets until the early 20th century because they were cheaper and could be erected swiftly.

Above Thomas Telford reckoned his iron arch Mythe Bridge, in Gloucestershire, to be 'the most handsomest bridge which has been built under my direction'. It was opened in 1826 and strengthened in 1992.

IRON RAILWAY BRIDGES

For years, the distinction of being the world's oldest surviving iron railway bridge has been accorded by scholars to the Gaunless Viaduct (1825), on display at the National Railway Museum, York (UK). Designed by George Stephenson for the first railway, the 23km (37 miles) between Stockton and Darlington in northeast England, it consists of four 4m (12.5ft) lenticular truss spans with curved top and bottom chord members of 2.5in (6cm) diameter wrought-iron rods and five vertical iron posts cast integrally with the wrought-iron chord members. In the last 20 years an older bridge has been discovered in South Wales at Merthyr Tydfil, a major early 19th century iron-producing centre. Pont-y-Cafnau (Bridge of Troughs) is a unique cast-iron combined aqueduct tramroad bridge below the confluence of the Taff and Taff Fechan, built between January and June 1793 by Watkin George, Chief Engineer of the Cyfarthfa Ironworks, to carry an edge railway and water channel. An iron trough-like girder is carried in an A-frame truss of cast iron spanning 14.2m (47ft), held together by mortise-and-tenon and dovetail joints. The next extant iron railway bridge seems to be another recently discovered at Aberdare (1811), followed by Gaunless. The oldest still in service is Hall's Station Bridge, a Howe truss designed in 1846 by Richard Osborne, who worked as engineer for the Philadelphia & Reading Railroad, although its current use is vehicular and not rail. The first major iron truss with pin connections was built in the USA in 1859 and the earliest iron cantilever in Germany in 1867, over the Main at Hassfurt.

Another important composite iron truss surviving from the early period of iron bridge construction is the Bollman Bridge (c1869) at Savage, Maryland (USA). The Britannia Bridge (1850) across the Menai Straits, Wales (see pages 128-131), designed by Robert Stephenson and William Fairbairn, was the prototype of the plate-girder bridge, eventually used throughout the world. Originally intended to be a stiffened suspension bridge of four spans, each span consisted of paired rectangular wrought-iron tubes through which the trains passed. Although Navier published his theory of elasticity in 1826, so little was known of structural theory that Stephenson relied primarily on empirical methods of testing, modifying and retesting a series of models to design the tubes. They were fabricated on site, floated into position and raised into place by hydraulic jacks. Riveting was done both by hand and using pneumatic riveting machines invented by Fairbairn. So strong were the tubes that the suspension chains were abandoned. The bridge continued in service until irreparably damaged by fire in May 1970. However, the near-contemporary Conway Castle Bridge (1848) survives (see pages 128-131).

Although the 19th century was marked by significant technological progress, such breathtaking achievement had its price. Three-quarters of the way through the century, two events, one on either side of the Atlantic, sobered the engineering profession. These took the form of accidents: the Ashtabula, Ohio, bridge disaster of 1876 in the USA and the Tay Bridge disaster in Scotland in 1879. Forewarnings had occurred in Europe as early as 1847, when one of Robert Stephenson's composite cast and wrought-iron girder bridges over the River Dee on the Chester & Holyhead Railway collapsed. Three years later, 478 French soldiers were pitched into the Maine at Angers, France, when one of the anchoring cables of a suspension bridge embedded in concrete tore loose during a storm, mainly owing to resonance oscillation and by the oxidation of the iron wires. The Dee Bridge disaster spurred the development of malleable wrought-iron girders, thought to be of safer construction. The collapse of the Basse-Chaine Bridge resulted in a 20-year moratorium on cable-suspension bridge construction in continental Europe.

BRIDGE DESIGN DURING THE 19TH CENTURY

It took the worst bridge disasters of the century in the USA, Great Britain and France to usher in the development of standards, specifications and enough regulation to protect the travelling public. The loss of 83 lives caused by the collapse of a cast- and wrought-iron truss

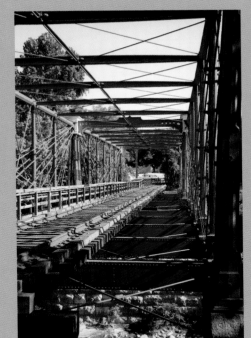

Above The Bollman Truss Railroad Bridge is one of the oldest standing iron railroad bridges in the US. Spanning the Little Patuxent River, it was constructed in 1869 and is listed on the National Register of Historic Places.

in Ashtabula prompted an investigation by the American Society of Civil Engineers. The loss of 80 lives by failure of a section of the Tay Bridge resulted in similar inquiries.

The reasons for these major failures were similar. An ignorance of metallurgy resulted in uneven manufacturing methods and defective castings and inadequate inspection and maintenance were inherent at both bridges. For the Tay Bridge, exceptionally strong vibrations due to dynamic wind stresses under a moving load created a lack of aerostatic stability and eventual failure. It took engineers another quarter-century to perfect bridge design according to advanced theories of stress analysis, understanding of material properties and renewed respect for the forces of nature. A definitive understanding of the physical oscillations and vibrations of structures did not occur until the middle of the 20th century after the Tacoma Bridge collapse in the USA in 1940 (see page 213).

Advances in design theory, graphic statics and a knowledge of the strength of materials by engineers such as Karl Culmann and Squire Whipple were achieved in the second half of the 19th century, but the factor that most influenced the scientific design of bridges was the railroads. Engineers had to know the precise amount of stresses in bridge members to accommodate the thundering impact of locomotives. Founded on the pioneering work of the American Squire Whipple and other European engineers as Collignon, the last quarter of the 19th century witnessed a broad application of both analytical and graphical analysis, testing of full-size components, comprehensive stress tables, standardized structural sections, metallurgical analysis, precision manufacturing and fabrication in bridge shops, publication of industry-wide standards, plans and specifications, inspections, and systematic cooperation between engineers, contractors, manufacturers and workers. The

Below The remnants of the High Girders section of the first Tay Bridge. Sub-standard materials combined with several design flaws meant it could not stand up to a violent storm on 28th December 1879.

combined experience of the railroads, bridge manufacturing companies and the engineering communities enabled the railroads successfully to tackle long-span iron and steel bridges and long-span trussed-roof train sheds, which became engineering icons of the 19th century.

NEW ADVANCES AND SCIENTIFIC ANALYSIS

The first practical design solution towards producing safe structures was obtained independently in the USA by Squire Whipple in 1847 and in Russia by D. I. Jourawski in 1850. Whipple had been working on the problem since before 1841, when he patented and built his all-iron bowstring truss bridge, which proved exceptionally suitable for short highway and canal spans. His book on stress analysis, *A Work on Bridge Building*, is recognized as the USA's contribution to structural mechanics for the period. His major breakthrough was the realisation that truss members could be analysed as a system of forces in equilibrium, assuming that a joint is a frictionless pin. Forces are broken down into horizontal and vertical components whose sums are in equilibrium. Known as the 'method of joints', it permits the determination of stresses in all members of a truss if two forces are known. Whipple clearly outlined methods, both analytical and graphical, for solving determinate trusses considering uniformly distributed dead loads and moving live loads. Over a dozen of Whipple's bowstring trusses survive as elegant illustrations of his breakthrough conclusions. The next advance was the 'method of sections' published in 1862 by A Ritter, a German engineer. Ritter simplified the calculations of forces by developing very simple formulae for determining the forces in the members intersected by a cross-section. The third advance was a better method of graphical analysis, developed independently by James Clerk Maxwell, Professor of Natural Philosophy at King's College, Cambridge (UK), published in 1864 and Karl Culmann, Professor at the newly established Federal Institute of Technology (Eidgenossische Technische Hochschule) in Zürich, who published his methods in 1866.

Enlightenment towards an ability to understand the way in which a cantilever bends and responds to certain stresses was developed over a long period of time, starting with Galileo's famous illustration of the wooden beam, anchored in the ruinous masonry wall, holding a stone weight at its end. Although it was not entirely accurate, subsequent solutions were discussed in terms of Galileo's cantilever. In 1776, C. A. Coulomb in France hypothesized in 1776 that the flexural stress in a cantilevered beam had a maximum value in compression on the bottom edge and a maximum value in tension on the top with a neutral axis somewhere between the two surfaces. The problem of understanding bending moments in mechanical terms was described by Louis Marie Henri Navier in his *Résumé de leçons données à l'École des Ponts et Chaussées* in 1826. In 1757, the Swiss mathematician Leonard Euler provided the solution to the elastic buckling of columns by deriving a formula that stated the maximum load a column could handle without collapsing.

RAILROAD VIADUCTS AND TRESTLES

Railroads, the transportation mode that revolutionized the 19th century, generated a bridge type that merits special attention. The limited traction of locomotives forced railroad engineers to design the line with easy gradients. Viaducts and trestles were the engineering solution for maintaining a nearly straight and horizontal line where the depth and width of the valley or gorge rendered embankments impracticable. These massive, elevated structures were first built in Roman style of multiple-stone arches and piers. Later, when wrought iron and steel became available, engineers built viaducts and trestles of great length and height on a series of truss spans or girders borne by individual framed towers composed of two or more bents braced together.

The Thomas Viaduct on the Baltimore & Ohio Railroad (1835), the Canton on the Boston & Providence Railroad (1835) and the Starrucca on the New York & Erie Railroad (1848) are the oldest stone viaducts and three of the great monumental structures of the USA's early

Above The slender brick piers of the Balcombe Viaduct (also known as the Ouse Valley Viaduct). Still in use, 11 million bricks were used in its construction, all imported from the Netherlands.

Below The Starrucca Viaduct in Pennsylvania was built in 1848 and is still in use as a rail bridge today. It is considered to be one of the first uses of concrete in US bridge construction.

27

Above The wrought and cast iron structure of the Meldon Viaduct, Dartmoor (UK) was built in 1874. It was closed as a rail bridge in the 1960s but reopened in 2002 as part of the Okehampton to Lydford walk and cycle route.

railways. Examples in Europe include the Viaduc de Barentine (1846), constructed by British navvies under the direction of MacKenzie and Thomas Brassey in brick rather than stone and the Viaduc de Saint-Chamas (1847), both in France. In the United Kingdom, notable viaducts include the 55m (181ft) Ballochmyle Viaduct (1848), designed by John Miller for the Glasgow & South Western Railway, the largest masonry-arch span in the country; the Harrington Viaduct (1876), the longest at 1,067m (3,500ft), carried on 82 brick arches; the Meldon Viaduct (1874), the best surviving iron viaduct in Devon; and, in concrete, the Glenfinnian Viaduct (1898), which has 21 arches of mass-poured concrete.

Most notable of the early trestles was the Portage Viaduct in the USA (1852), a remarkable timber structure designed by Silas Seymour, carrying the Erie Railroad over the Genessee River, 71m (234ft) above the water and 276m (876ft) long. It was destroyed by fire in 1875, to be replaced in iron and later in steel. One of the first iron viaducts was the 510m (1,673ft) long Crumlin Viaduct (1857), constructed by Thomas W. Kennard and designed by Charles Liddell for the Newport-Hereford line, 66m (217ft) above the Ebbw Vale in Wales. It served as the prototype for later ones, such as the Viaduc de la Bouble (1871), a series of lattice girders on cast-iron towers flared at the bottom, built under the direction of Wilhelm Nordling. It was 395m (1,296ft) long by 66m (216ft) high on the Commentry-Gannett line in France.

The first viaduct of iron in the USA was designed by Albert Fink for the Baltimore & Ohio Railroad over Tray Run in the Cheat River valley in (West) Virginia, a remote, wild, yet picturesque site in the wilderness. Dating from 1853, it was a series of inclined cast-iron columns resting on stone pedestals connected at the top by cast-iron arches, the whole system braced by wrought-iron ties. Examples today in North America include the Lethbridge Viaduct (1909) on the Canadian Pacific in Alberta (composed of alternating 20m (67ft) trestles and 30m (100ft) girders, at 1,624m (5,327ft) long the longest and heaviest in the world) and the Kinzua Viaduct (1900) on the former Erie Railroad in Pennsylvania which was partially destroyed by a freak tornado in 2003. The Tunkhannock Viaduct (1915), 73m high (240ft) by 724m long (2,375ft), is the largest reinforced concrete-arch bridge in the world.

SUSPENSION BRIDGES

Although suspension bridges had been known in China as early as 206BC, the first chain suspension bridge did not appear in Europe until 1741, when the 21m (70ft) span Winch Bridge was constructed over a chasm of the River Tees, with the flooring laid directly on two chains. It was an American, James Finley, however, who built the first practical suspension bridge in 1796 in the USA. This was a bridge over Jacobs Creek near Uniontown, Pennsylvania, which Finley described as a 'stiffened' bridge in an article he published in *Portfolio* in 1810. The span displayed all the essential elements of the modern suspension bridge: a level deck hung from a catenary system (the shape of a hanging flexible chain when acted upon by its own weight) suspended over towers and anchored in the ground, and a truss-stiffened deck, resulting in a rigid bridge capable of supporting relatively heavy loads.

THE DEVELOPMENT OF WIRE CABLING

The world's first wire-cable suspension bridge was a 124m (408ft) temporary footbridge built in 1816 for the workers of wire manufacturers Josiah White and Erskine Hazard over the Schuylkill in Philadelphia. The USA contributed little more until the middle of the century, but these inventions were immediately followed up in Europe. The French and Swiss continued to use wire cables, developing methods of fabricating the cables *in situ*. In 1822, Marc Séguin proposed a suspension cable made up of 100 thin iron wires, erected his first suspension bridge (actually a catwalk like the White and Hazard bridge) over the Cance at Annonay in France, and proposed a major structure over the Rhône at Tournon. Through scientific testing, Séguin proved the strength of the wire cable – twice that of the English iron eyebar chain – and described his research in *Des ponts en fil de fer*, published in 1824. The

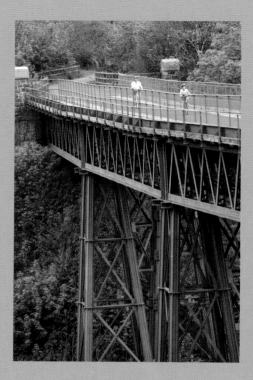

Above The highest surviving railway viaduct in the UK, Ballochmyle Viaduct crosses 55m (181ft) above the River Ayr. It was completed in 1848 for the Glasgow, Paisley Kilmarnock and Ayr Railway.

Right Closed permanently to trains in 2002, the Kinzua Viaduct was destroyed by a freak tornado in 2003; nine of the original twenty surviving towers are currently being evaluated for stabilisation.

Above Marc Séguin was the inventor of the wire-cable suspension bridge and his 1847 pedestrian bridge over the Rhône is the oldest of its type in the world. It replaced a previous structure of 1825, also by Séguin.

world's first permanent wire-cable suspension bridge, designed by Séguin and Guillaume-Henri Dufour, was opened to the public in Geneva in 1823, followed by Séguin's Tain-Tournon Bridge, a double suspension span over the Rhône, completed in 1825. Its 1847 replacement still stands, probably the oldest wire-cable suspension bridge in the world, with its carefully replicated wooden stiffening truss and deck. Several of Séguin's first-generation wire-cable suspension bridges, dating from the 1830s, remain over the Rhône at Andance and Fourques, but the decks have been replaced with steel. Wire cable attained its place as the system *par excellence* for long-span bridges in 1834, with the 265m (870ft) Fribourg Bridge, designed by Joseph Chaley over the Sarine in Switzerland. From this developed the typical European standard – cables of parallel, thin wires, light decks stiffened by wooden trusses, piers and abutments sunk – using hydraulic cement – of which hundreds were built.

LINKED EYEBARS

At the time British engineers preferred to use chains of linked eyebars and achieved spans of lightness and grace, all the more effective in contrast with the colossal masonry suspension towers. The UK's first large-scale suspension bridge was the Menai Bridge on the London to Holyhead road over the straits of the same name in North Wales. Travellers would board a ship at Holyhead for the final leg of the trip to Ireland. It was designed by Thomas Telford and completed in 1826, with an unprecedented span of 177m (580ft) using wrought-iron eyebars, each bar being carefully tested before being pinned together and lifted into place. The roadway was only 7m (24ft) wide and, without stiffening trusses, soon proved highly unstable in the wind. The Menai Bridge was twice rebuilt before the entire suspension system was replicated in steel in 1940 and the arched openings in the towers were widened. The oldest suspension bridge extant today is the Union Bridge over the River Tweed at Berwick (UK), a chain-link bridge designed and erected by Captain Samuel Brown in 1820, with a span of 137m (449ft).

ROEBLING'S SUSPENSION BRIDGES

With the French declaring a moratorium on suspension-bridge construction following the collapse of the Basse-Chaine Bridge in 1850, the creative edge passed back across the Atlantic, to be picked up by Charles Ellet and John Augustus Roebling in the USA. After studying suspension bridges in France, Ellet returned with the technology and built a 308m (1,010ft) bridge over the Ohio River at Wheeling, (West) Virginia, in 1849, which was the longest in the world. Thanks to techniques developed by the Roeblings and used in the structure's rebuilding, following a storm that ripped the cables off their saddles, the bridge remains in service today.

Roebling had arrived in the USA 10 years earlier and established a wire-rope factory in Saxonburg, Pennsylvania, which he later moved to Trenton, New Jersey. Educated in Europe, he would have been exposed to the concepts of wire-cable suspension bridge engineering of the French and Swiss. He and Ellet competed for primacy in suspension bridge design. Roebling won out when he took over design of the Niagara Suspension Bridge from Ellet, successfully completing it in 1855.

The inherent tendency of suspension bridges to sway and undulate in wavelike motions under repeated rhythmic loads such as marching soldiers or the wind was not completely understood by engineers until the 1940s, following the collapse of the Tacoma Narrows Bridge ('Galloping Gertie'). The credit for designing the first suspension bridge rigid enough to withstand wind loads and the highly concentrated loadings of locomotives belongs to John Roebling. His first masterpiece was the Niagara Suspension Bridge, with a span of 250m (821ft) on the Grand Trunk Railway below Niagara Falls. The two decks, the upper for the railway and the lower for common road service, were separated by a 6m (18ft) stiffening truss. In addition, the truss was braced with radiating cable stays inclined from the tops

Above Also known as the Chain Bridge, the Union Bridge over the River Tweed was the longest wrought-iron bridge in the world when it opened in 1820. Today, it is the oldest suspension bridge still open to traffic.

Above The footcarriage way of Roebling's double-decker Niagara Falls Suspension Bridge ran underneath the railway. The entire bridge was replaced by the Whirlpool Rapids Bridge in 1897.

Above Tightrope walker Maria Spelterini, wearing peach baskets on her feet, crosses the Niagara River Gorge in 1876. In the background, hundreds of spectators stand watching from the Niagara Falls Suspension Bridge.

of the suspension towers and anchoring cables tying the deck to the sides of the gorge, arresting any tendency to lift under gusts of wind. For the four main cables, Roebling used parallel wires laid up in place but, instead of individual strands like the 'garland' system preferred by the French, he bunched the strands together in a single large cable and wrapped them with wire, a technique he patented in 1841 but one that Vicat had illustrated in 1831 in his *Rapport sur les ponts en fil de fer sur le Rhône*.

THE MAGNIFICENT BROOKLYN BRIDGE
Few bridges in the world built since the Brooklyn Bridge in New York can stand entirely clear of its shadow. Completed in 1883, the plan involved two distinctive stone towers, four main cables, anchorages, diagonal stay cables and four stiffening trusses separating the common roadway and trolley line from a pedestrian promenade. With a record-breaking span of 486m (1,595ft), the Brooklyn Bridge was designed by John Roebling, but it was built by his son and daughter-in-law after he died of blood poisoning following an accident while surveying the location of the Manhattan tower in which his foot was crushed. Massive Egyptian towers, pierced by pointed Gothic arches, stand 84m (276.5ft) above mean high water and 24m (78.5ft) below on the Manhattan side, 13.6m (44.5ft) on the Brooklyn. Diagonal stay cables give the bridge its distinctive appearance, but actually function to stiffen the deck.

Two other Roebling suspension bridges survive – one spanning the Ohio River at Cincinnati was completed in 1867. The 1849 Delaware Aqueduct was designed to carry a wooden trunk of water on the Delaware & Hudson Canal. The latter was carefully rehabilitated by the US National Park Service and is the oldest surviving suspension bridge in the USA.

Above The massive masonry towers of Roebling's Brooklyn Bridge were so tall that foundations 24m (78.5ft) deep had to be dug below the water level to accommodate them.

STEEL BRIDGES
Structural steel is stronger and more supple than cast or wrought iron and allowed greater design flexibility. The last 30 years of the 19th century witnessed the phasing in of steel plates and rolled shapes, leading to the enormous production of steel trusses and plate-girder spans of ever-increasing lengths throughout the world. Steel arches and cantilevers were favoured for long spans because they better withstood the impact, vibration and concentrated loads of heavy rail traffic.

STRONGER AND FURTHER
The earliest known use of steel in bridge construction was the 102m (334ft) suspension span across the Danube Canal (1828) near Vienna (Austria), designed by Ignaz von Mitis. The steel eye-bar chains were forged from decarburized iron from Styria (the largest of the nine Austrian states). Steel halved the weight of wrought iron, but remained prohibitively expensive for another 40 years before steelmaking processes such as the Bessemer and the open-hearth were perfected (it is uncertain whether the Styrian ironmasters created real steel or whether the decarburisation was a mechanical process resulting in a surface-hardened steel, a kind of wrought iron rather than the mass steel that results from the Bessemer process). The first major bridge utilising true steel was the Eads Bridge (1874), the most graceful of the Mississippi River crossings in the USA, built by the Keystone Bridge Company, which subcontracted fabrication of the steel parts to the Butcher Steel Works and the iron parts to Carnegie-Kloman, both of Pittsburgh. Its ribbed, tubular steel arch spans of 153m, 159m and 153m (502ft, 520ft and 502ft) and double-decked design shattered all engineering precedents for the time: the centre span was by far the longest arch. Mathematical formulae for the design were developed by Charles Pfeiffer. The cantilever method of erection, devised by Colonel Henry Flad and used for the first time in the USA, eliminated the centring that would have been impossible in the wide, deep and fast-flowing Mississippi. While recovering from illness in France, the designer James Buchanan Eads provided a method to sinking piers in deep water. He investigated a bridge under construction over the Allier at Vichy that used Cubitt and Wright's pneumatic caissons – floorless chambers filled with compressed air.

Above The longest bridge arch bridge in the world at the time of it completion (1874), the Eads Bridge, St Louis (USA), was also the first exclusive use of cantilever support in a bridge. It is still in use today.

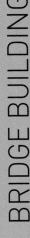

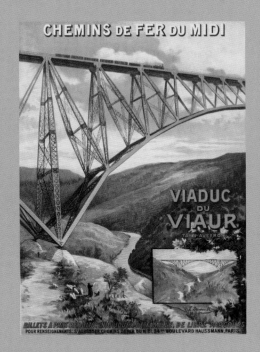

Above The Viaur Viaduct cantilever railroad bridge was the first major use of steel in France. Construction took seven years between 1895 and 1902 led by engineer Paul Joseph Bodin.

Left The construction of the Hell Gate Bridge, originally called the New York Connecting Railroad Bridge, took two years from 1914 to 1916. It is thought to be the inspiration for the Sydney Harbour Bridge (1932).

The first major bridge of steel in France was the Viaur Viaduct (1902), a three-hinged steel arch of 220m (721ft) flanked by 95m (311ft) cantilevers. The crowning achievement of the material during the 19th century, however, was the mighty Forth Railway Bridge in Scotland (1890, see pages 138-141). Its design was motivated by the Tay Bridge disaster. About 54,000 tonnes of Siemens-Martin open-hearth steel were required for the 521m (1,710ft) cantilever spans whose main compression struts of rolled steel plate were riveted into 4m (12ft) diameter tubes. Another authority on the effects of wind on structures was Gustav Eiffel, who conducted similar experiments in France prior to designing another of the world's great arch bridges, the 165m (541ft) Garabit Viaduct (1885) in the windy valleys of the Massif Central, though he held to wrought iron, not being entirely convinced by the new material.

General steel arches of enormous span were built during the first few decades of the 20th century. One of the greatest is the Hell Gate Bridge in the USA (1917), a two-hinged trussed arch, the top chord of which serves as part of a stiffening truss. Designed by Gustav Lindenthal to span the Hell Gate at the northern tip of Manhattan Island for the New England Connecting Railroad, it is framed between two massive stone towers. The 298m (978ft) arch, weighing 80,000 tonnes, was the longest and heaviest steel arch in the world. The next was Bayonne Bridge (1931), which remains one of the longest steel arches in the world today. It was built during the Depression by a team assembled under the direction of Swiss-born and educated engineer, Othmar Ammann, chief engineer of the Port Authority of New York. Opening just three weeks after the George Washington Bridge, then the longest suspension bridge in the world, this second record-breaking span was financed and built by the Port Authority simultaneously, the two projects forming one of the greatest public work endeavours since Roman times. The Bayonne Bridge connects Bayonne (New Jersey) and Staten Island (New York) with a manganese-steel parabolic two-hinged arch of 511m (1,675ft) span and 81m (266ft) rise, the deck clearing high water by 46m (150ft). As in the Hell Gate, the arch's top chord acts as a stiffener, with the bottom chord carrying the load. The Bayonne Bridge was designed to be 8m (25ft) longer than the nearly identical Sydney Harbour Bridge in Australia, started five years earlier.

Bridge building prospered in areas other than Europe and the USA because colonial empires of several nations were at their peak during the autumn years of the 19th century. In India, for example, the British built several long-span railway bridges, such as the Hooghly and the Sukkur bridges that exceeded 300m (1,000ft) in span and are interesting because they were constructed using the simplest equipment and armies of unskilled labour.

CANTILEVER BRIDGES

As mentioned, two of the best examples of the cantilever structure form are the Eads Bridge, where the erection of the arches employed principles of the cantilever and the Forth Railway Bridge, perhaps the world's greatest cantilever. An examination of this type of bridge is warranted because of its engineering interest and because it illustrates the outstanding application of iron and steel in bridge construction.

THE FIRST CANTILEVERS

Cantilevers were one of the first bridge types, many being built by the ancient cultures of China and India. The first modern cantilever was Heinrich Gerber's Hassfurt Bridge over the Main in Germany (1867), with a central span of 38m (124ft). According to W. Westhofen, who wrote the classic account of the Forth Bridge, the idea was first suggested by John Fowler, co-designer of the Forth Bridge, around 1846-50. In Britain and the USA the form was known as cantilevers, in France as portes-à-faux and in Germany as the Gerber Bridge, named after the builder. By inserting hinges, the continuous girder can be made statically determinant (the internal forces acting on the structure are sufficient for equilibrium). This was their first attribute, but later as the possibility of erection without scaffolding was recognized – the

Above The Bayonne Bridge, New Jersey (USA), succeeded the Hell Gate Bridge as the longest steel arch bridge in the world when it opened in 1932. The design of the arch was based on its New York predecessor.

BRIDGE BUILDING

Above Canadian daredevil Samuel J. Dixon crosses the Niagara River under Schneider's Niagara Cantilever Bridge in 1890. C. C. Schneider also investigated the collapse of the first Quebec Bridge in 1907.

Above The Forth Rail Bridge (1890) comprises two main cantilevered spans. It was designed to withstand conditions far in excess of those that caused the Tay Bridge disaster in 1879.

ability of the arms of the bridge to be built out from the piers, balancing each other without the need for falsework which became the great advantage. The principle also is applicable to other bridge types such as arches, an example being the Eads Bridge, where the width, depth, and current of the mighty Mississippi prevented the erection of falsework.

In 1877, C. Shaler Smith provided the first practical test of the principle when he built what then was the world's longest cantilever over a 366m (1,200ft) wide and 84m (275ft) deep gorge of the Kentucky River near Dixville, Kentucky (USA). The cantilever resolved the difficulty of erecting falsework in a deep wide gorge. The anchor arms were 11m (37.5ft) deep Whipple trusses that extended 23m (75ft) beyond the piers. From these were hung 91m (300ft) semi-floating trusses fixed at the abutments and hinged to the cantilever, making the overall span from pier to abutment 114m (375ft). The bridge was rebuilt in 1911 by Gustav Lindenthal using the identical span lengths, but with trusses twice as deep.

The next important cantilever was a counterbalanced span designed by C C Schneider for the Michigan Central Railroad over the Niagara Gorge in 1883. With arms supporting a simple suspended truss, this 151m (495ft) span and the nearly identical Fraser River span in British Columbia (Canada) directed the attention of the engineering world to this new type of bridge. These two were the prototypes for subsequent cantilevers at Poughkeepsie, New York, the Firth of Forth Bridge in Scotland and the Québec Bridge in Canada.

The Poughkeepsie Cantilever (1886) was the first rail crossing of the Hudson River below Albany, 89km (55 miles) north of New York City. Built by the Union Bridge Company of New York to designs by company engineers Francis O'Rourke and Pomeroy P. Dickinson, the overall length is 2,063m (6,768ft), including two cantilevers of 167m (548ft) each. Strengthened in 1906 by adding a third line of trusses down the middle designed by Ralph Modjeski, this magnificent structure was closed and abandoned in 1974.

The world's most famous cantilever also is one of the world's first and largest steel bridges and held the record for longest cantilever for 27 years. Bridge enthusiasts are familiar with the brilliant demonstration used by Sir Benjamin Baker to illustrate the structural principles of the Firth of Forth Bridge: two men sitting on chairs with outstretched arms and sticks supporting Kaichi Watanabe, a visiting engineering student from Japan, sitting on a board, representing the fixed piers, cantilevers and suspended span. To ensure that there was no repeat of the Tay disaster, Baker conducted a series of tests, gauging wind at several sites in the area over a two-year period, arriving at a design pressure of 274kg/m² (56lb/ft²), which was considerably in excess of any load the bridge would ever sustain. Each of the two main spans of the bridge consists of two cantilevers of 207m (680ft) with a suspended span of 107m (350ft) for a total length of 521m (1,710ft). John Fowler and Benjamin Baker designed the Forth Bridge (1890) to resist wind loads 5.5 times those that toppled the Tay Bridge.

The Forth Rail Bridge's record was broken in 1917, when the Québec Bridge was finally completed, spanning the St. Lawrence River near Québec (Canada) with a 549m (1,800ft) cantilever span (see pages 210-213). Its predecessor failed in 1907 while under construction, killing more than 80 workmen and ending the career of one of America's most prominent engineers. Theodore Cooper had taken the commission reluctantly with a fee insufficient to hire assistants, to allow for written specifications, or to provide for on-site inspections. The design was not recalculated when Cooper, intent on exceeding the span of the record-holding Forth Bridge, increased it by approximately 61m (200ft), which was ultimately to result in the failure of one of the main compression members of the lower chord in the south anchor. The second bridge also had its problems as well when one of the jacks failed while lifting the 5,000-tonne centre suspended span, dropping it into the river. A duplicate truss was successfully lifted into place within two weeks and the bridge was finally opened. This

Right The Poughkeepsie Cantilever Bridge (USA) was decommissioned in 1974. The structure, which crosses the Hudson River, is under repair and reconstruction and there are hopes to reopen it as a pedestrian walkway.

bridge, designed by E. H. Duggan and Phelps Johnson with Ralph Modjeski as consultant, was criticized by many engineers as being the ugliest, while the cantilever was generally regarded as a type, especially those of American origin, whose profile was unsightly despite their record lengths. The largest cantilever in Europe was Saligney's Danube Bridge near Czernavoda (Romania), with a span of 190m (623ft). Another great cantilever is the Howrah Bridge over the Hooghly River at Kolcata in India (see pages 182-183)

THE REINTRODUCTION OF MASONRY AND CONCRETE

Concrete is an ancient material. It was first discovered and used by the Romans in their aqueducts and temples, to be sporadically rediscovered throughout time by engineers who used it in its mass-poured form. The discovery of natural cement in 1796, on the Isle of Sheppey in the Thames Estuary (UK), renewed interest in the material, but the age of concrete began its most vigorous development with Joseph Aspdin's invention of artificial Portland cement in 1824. This mixture of clay and limestone, calcined and ground, resulted in a material having broad application for buildings and bridges. The scientific studies of Vicat on natural and artificial cements initiated in 1816 at the Pont de Souillac in France revealed the first understanding of the chemical properties of hydraulic cement. Canvass White, an engineer on the Erie Canal (USA), discovered natural cement in 1818 and established a mill to manufacture the substance at Chittenango, New York. The primary benefit of the material was its ability to set under water. Naming it hydraulic cement, he patented the process in 1819 and used it for aqueducts, abutments, culverts and lock walls.

In 1831, Lebrun, a French engineer, designed the first concrete bridge to span the River Agout, although it never was built. A significant early structural use of concrete in the USA was in 1848 for the foundations and deck of the Starrucca Viaduct on the New York & Erie Railroad, a mighty stone-arched bridge with an overall length of 317m (1,040ft), designed by Julius Walker Adams and built by James Pugh Kirkwood.

Later, the use of artificial cement combined with more sophisticated understanding of the mathematical principles of arch theory resulted in renewed interest in stone and masonry arch bridges in Europe. Beginning in the mid-19th century, masonry railroad viaducts were an important civil engineering technology for continental Europe. The most impressive were the 600m (1,969ft) long Chaumont Viaduct (1857) and the 73m (240ft) high Sainte-Brieuc (Barentin) Viaduct (1860), both in France and the Göltzschtal Viaduct in Germany, which used 26 million units of brick.

The French engineer, Paul Séjourne, expressed the most elegant modern restatement of the principles of this most ancient material in his masterpiece bridges of stone, the 85m (279ft) span Pont Adolphe in Luxembourg (1903) and the bridge at Plauen, Germany (1905), which was the longest ever achieved in stone masonry, with a span of 90m (295ft).

CONCRETE AS MAINSTREAM

The beginning of concrete as a major material of bridge construction dates from 1865, when it was used in its mass, unreinforced form for a multiple-arch structure on the Grand Maître Aqueduct conveying water from the River Vanne 151km (94 miles) to Paris. Engineers in the late 19th century demonstrated the possibilities of reinforced concrete as a structural material. With concrete resisting compressive forces and wrought iron and steel bars carrying tension, bridges of dramatic sweeping curves began to evolve. Today's long-span reinforced-concrete bridges are descended from the efforts of French gardener Joseph Monier's numerous bridge patents granted between 1868 and 1878. He is credited with being the first to understand the principles of reinforced concrete when, in 1867, he patented plant tubs of cement mortar strengthened with iron-wire mesh embedded in the concrete and moulded into curvilinear forms. Not being an engineer, he was not permitted to build bridges

Above After six years of construction, the Howrah Bridge was opened in 1943. One of three bridges that cross the Hooghly River, it has become one of the most famous symbols of Kolkata and West Bengal.

Above The 78m (256ft) high Göltzschtal Viaduct in Saxony, Germany, was engineered by Johann Andreas Schubert and Robert Wilke, is one of the largest brick-built bridges in the world.

Above The tallest piers of the Chaumont Viaduct rise 50m (164ft) above the valley floor; four of them were rebuilt in concrete (and covered by stone) after being blown up by German forces in 1944.

in France and so he sold his patents to German and Austrian contractors Wayss, Freitag and Schuster, who built the first generation of reinforced-concrete bridges in Europe: the Monierbrau 40m (131ft) footbridge in Bremen (Germany) and the Wildegg Bridge, with a span of 37m (121ft), in Switzerland. Additional patents were granted in Belgium, France and Italy, especially to the Frenchman François Hennebique, who established the first international firm to market his bridges before the First World War. His first masterpiece was built at Millesimo (Italy) in 1898, and that at Châtellérault in France (1900) remains as one of the first notable reinforced-concrete arch bridges in the world, with a central span of 52m (172ft) and two lateral arches of 40m (131ft). In 1912, Hennebique set a new world record with a bridge over the Tiber in Rome (Italy) with a span of 100m (328ft). Other important three-span bridges with impressive central spans were built in France by Eugène Freyssinet, such as the bridges at Veurdre (1910) and Boutiron (1912).

FRENCH INFLUENCES

In France, where much of the original thinking on reinforced concrete occurred, the record span was the Saint-Pierre du Vauvray Bridge (1922) by Freyssinet. He perfected the technique of prestressing concrete by inserting hydraulic rams in a gap left at the crown of arches, then activating the rams to lift the arches off the falsework and filling the gap with concrete, leaving only permanent compressive stresses in the arches. The Vauvray Bridge over the Seine was the record span at 131m (430ft), the deck being hung from hollow cellular arch ribs on wire hangers, coated with cement mortar and supporting the road on light concrete deck trusses. The Vauvray Bridge was destroyed in the Second World War, leaving the Plougastel Bridge (1930) over the River Elon at Brest, with three spans of 173m (567ft), as the longest reinforced-concrete arch span until 1942.

SWISS STRUCTURES

Swiss engineer Robert Maillart designed three-hinged arches in which the deck and the arch ribs were combined to produce closely integrated structures that evolved into stiffened arches of very thin reinforced concrete and concrete slabs, as at the Schwandbach Bridge (1933), near Schwarzenbach (Switzerland). Maillart's early apprenticeship with Hennebique sharpened his awareness of the plastic character of the material. His profound understanding of reinforced concrete allowed him to develop new, light and magnificently sculptural forms. Maillart's bridges are of two distinct types: stiffened-slab arches and three-hinged arches with an integrated road slab. The Salginatobel Bridge (1930) near Schiers (Switzerland) is the most spectacular example of this type of bridge in the world.

THE US AND THE UK

The world's longest concrete and masonry arch bridge is the Rockville Bridge (1902), which carries four tracks of the former Pennsylvania Railroad over the Susquehanna River (USA) on 48 arches, 21m (70ft) each, for a total length of 1,164m (3,820ft). It was part of a massive twenty-year improvement programme under the direction of William H. Brown, chief engineer. The largest all-reinforced concrete bridge, however, is the Tunkhannock Viaduct (1915) built by the Delaware, Lackawanna & Western Railroad in northeastern Pennsylvania (USA), composed of 10 semi-circular double-arch spans of 55m (180ft) with the spandrels filled with 11 smaller arches. Like Rockville, it was a major component in another early 20th century US railroad improvement project, this time a massive realignment. Abraham Burton Cohen was the rail line's designer of the reinforced-concrete bridges.

The first major reinforced-concrete bridge in the United Kingdom was the Royal Tweed Bridge (1928), made up of four rhythmic open-spandrel arches filled with vertical posts increasing in span from 51m (167ft) to 110m (361ft) as the roadway climbs from low to high embankments on each side of the river.

Above The Pont Adolphe by Paul Séjourne has become one of Luxembourg's national symbols and an important tourist attraction for Luxembourg City. To support its own weight, the structure makes use of reinforced concrete.

Above The reinforced concrete Saint-Pierre-du-Vauvray Bridge, France, was inaugurated in 1923. It was destroyed in 1940, during the Second World War, but later replaced with an almost identical structure.

BRIDGE BUILDING

SWEDISH CONTRIBUTIONS

Sweden is another country that excelled in building elegant and innovative reinforced-concrete arch bridges of extremely long span. The first was the Traneberg Bridge (1934) in Stockholm, designed by Harbour Board engineers Ernst Nilsson and S. Kasarnowsky with Eugène Freyssinet consulting. Its span, at 181m (593ft), was surpassed briefly in 1942 by the Esla Bridge in Spain with a span of 192m (631ft), but within the same year the title for the longest arch was regained for Sweden by S. Haggböm with the Sando Bridge, the longest reinforced- concrete arch in the world at 264m (866ft).

MOVABLE AND TRANSPORTER BRIDGES

Two seemingly modern types of bridge – the bascule and the transporter – are actually among the oldest types of bridge known. The bascule or draw span was developed by Europeans during the Middle Ages, but here was a resurgence of movable bridges during the late 19th century. Reliable electric motors and techniques for counterbalancing the massive weights of the bascule, lift, or swing spans marked the beginning of modern movable-bridge construction. They are usually found in flat terrain, where the cost of approaches to gain high-level crossings is prohibitive, and their characteristics include rapidity of operation, the ability to vary the openings depending on the size of vessels and the facility to build in congested areas adjacent to other bridges.

The completion of Tower Bridge over the Thames in London (1894), a roller-bearing trunnion bascule and the best-known bascule bridge in the world (see pages 134-137), and Van Buren Street Bridge in Chicago, the first rolling lift bridge in the USA (patented by William Scherzer), marks the efficient solution to problems of lifting and locking mechanisms. In 1914, the Canadian Pacific Railroad completed the world's largest double-leaf bascule, spanning 102m (336ft) over the ship canal at Sault-Sainte-Marie, Michigan, rebuilt with identical spans in 1941. The Saint Charles Airline Railway Bridge (1919) spanning 16th Street in Chicago was at 79m (260ft) the longest single-leaf bascule when it was completed.

In 1927, the Atchison, Topeka & Santa Fe Railroad built the world's longest single-span swing bridge, 160m (525ft), over the Mississippi at Fort Madison, Iowa (USA). One of the most interesting and unusual movable bridges is the Lacey V Murrow Bridge (1940), whose design reached back to the pontoons built by Roman legions. The depth and breadth of the lake precluded the construction of conventional piers on pilings, cantilever, or suspension spans, and so Washington State bridge engineers designed a floating bridge supported by hollow concrete pontoons to connect Seattle and Mercer Island. Equally unique was the retractable floating draw span for ocean-going ships in the lake. Three other bridges of this type were completed over the Hood Canal (1961) and at Evergreen Point (1963). A span parallel to the Murrow Bridge now carries the increased traffic of Interstate Highway 90.

TRANSPORTER BRIDGES

A comparable example of an unusual type of movable bridge in Europe is the transporter bridge, where a platform suspended by cables from tall towers and superstructure is carried on an overhead framework. This type of bridge also reaches back into history, integrating ancient technology such as the rope ferry with new structural forms and materials such as the iron beam and the strongest steel cables. The transporter bridge was the original solution to spanning the mouth of a river or entrance to a harbour and also served as a monumental gateway. Although it was patented in the UK and the USA in the mid 19th century, the first significant example was designed by the Basque architect and engineer Alberto de Palacio and built by French engineer Ferdinand Arnodin at Portugalete (1893) in Spain. Arnodin also invented the twisted steel cable, an important innovation for this type of bridge. The only other survivors are located in the United Kingdom at Middlesbrough and Newport and at Martrou in France.

Above The Middlesbrough Transporter Bridge (UK) carries a small car or gondola containing up to 200 people the length of its structure. It is the largest bridge of its kind in the world that still operates.

Above The name of the Pegasus Bridge (1935), France, is derived from the emblem worn by the British troops who took control of the bridge in 1944. The bascule bridge was replaced by an identical structure in 1994.

Above Constructred from white-painted wood, the Magere Brug (1934) crosses the River Amstel in the centre of Amsterdam (Netherland. Its relatively small structure has led locals to call it the 'skinny bridge'.

IN CONCLUSION: 20TH- AND 21ST-CENTURY BRIDGE BUILDING

A global review of bridge building would not be complete without comment on recent 20th century bridges, what new materials and design techniques promise for the future of bridge building, and a final word on the value and role that heritage and the preservation of older bridges holds as we enter the 21st century.

STRUCTURES KNOWN AND UNKNOWN

It should be said that 'unknown' bridges are in many ways just as important as the examples featured in this book. Occasionally, a landmark bridge is lost; either to natural or human-made disaster, and in some cases to neglect, whether willful or otherwise.

For example, organisations in the US are struggling to save the ubiquitous metal truss and concrete-arch spans, built in the late 19th and early 20th centuries. These bridges adorn the American countryside and cityscapes on scenic highways and byways and urban roads. In addition, there's the question of what to do with the post Second World War and early-interstate era bridges. Highway departments developed steel beam and cantilever bridges, concrete slabs and girders, reinforced- and prestressed-concrete beams for overpasses, short and mid-length spans, enabling the construction of interstate bridges in their thousands.

When the I-35W bridge in Minneapolis collapsed into the Mississippi River in 2007, the entire bridge engineering industry responded. It was the USA's worst bridge disaster

Above Santiago Calatrava's cable-stayed Sundial Bridge across the Sacramento River in Redding, California; the giant mast of the bridge serves as the world's largest sundial.

Below The collapsed section of the I-35W Mississippi River Bridge in August 2007 which claimed seven lives. The bridge was originally built in 1967 and reconstruction has already started on a replacement.

Above The Gateshead Millennium Bridge has won awards for its innovative eye-lid design. Its structure also blends very carefully with the surrounding architecture, including the Tyne Bridge (1928).

BRIDGE BUILDING

Above Santiago Calatrava's Alamillo Bridge in Seville, Spain; the weight of the single steel mast is enough to support the deck without the need for counter-stay cables on the opposite end of the structure.

since the failure of the Silver Bridge in 1967, and in particular it brought home to the historic bridge community the fact that the early interstate era is potentially the bridge population most at risk, rather than the earlier bridges that have been the focus of surveys, preservation and scholarship.

In the 21st century previously unknown bridges will continue to be discovered primarily in developing countries or parts of the world formerly closed off. One example is China, where woven wood timber and cantilevered covered bridges have been recently revealed to the rest of the world.

Even in long-industrialized countries such as the UK, discoveries occasionally appear. A prime example here is the Cornwallis Bridge (c1803), one of the first cast-iron bridges in the UK. It is one of the earliest examples distinguished because the iron arch ribs are hollow instead of solid. The bridge remained undiscovered until 1996, hidden behind reeds and undergrowth on a mile-long lake on the grounds of Culford Hall, Suffolk, which belonged to the second Marquis Cornwallis. This was an exceptionally important find because it has remained unmodified for over 200 years.

PROFESSIONALS AND ENTHUSIASTS

The US, like many other countries, is at a critical turning point in saving its historic bridges. Efforts over the past 30 years are slowly beginning to affect how old bridges are regarded. Some US highway departments and engineering firms possess the knowledge and skills to care for these structures and several state transport departments recognize that this forms part of their responsibility for comprehensive highway planning.

But the greatest phenomenon in the since the mid 1990s has been the general public's appreciation of historic bridges across the world. In recent years there has been a growth among private enthusiasts who have created sophisticated web sites cataloguing information and photographs of historic bridges, monitoring the status of surviving spans and individuals and groups fighting to preserve historic bridges in their communities.

HISTORIC VERSUS CONTEMPORARY

A new era of public concern of the impact of infrastructure on the environment is upon us. Though the current environmental and economic outlook does not appear very promising, the potential that infrastructure holds for shaping architectural and urban form is still being realised. Bridges and their settings have an inherent spatial and functional order that serve as the most important components of design, both architectural and engineering, that establishes an identity and has a tangible relationship with the community, region or country. Infrastructure can be designed with a formal clarity that expresses its importance to safety, while at the same time creating new layers of urban landmarks, spaces and connections. In addition to championing the preservation of historic bridges, contemporary bridge design that exemplifies creative and artistic flair should be celebrated and promoted.

CONTEMPORARY BRIDGES

Alamillo Bridge (1992) in Seville, by the Spanish engineer/architect Santiago Calatrava (see pages 94–97), is but one of many examples of the engineers' potential of an artistic, inventive approach to design. Calatrava's designs display not only distinctive visual style but urbanism, a way of building that infuses spirit in public works.

Another example of modern bridge design is Le Pont de Normandie (1995). One of the reasons the French decided to build the world's longest cable-stayed bridge was motivated by national pride. Le Pont de Normandie had beaten the record held by the Skarnsundet Bridge of 539m (1,740ft) set in 1991. At the time of writing, the world record for the longest cable-

Above The Pont de Normandie, France, was the world's longest cable-stayed bridge, overtaking the previous record-holder, the Skarnsundet Bridge in Norway, and stretching a full 42 per cent further.

stayed suspension bridge, the Tartara Bridge (1999) in Hiroshima, Japan, was exceeded by the Sutong Bridge (2008) in the same country. It will be exceeded by others.

Critical factors in the development of superstructures such as the Alamillo, Pont de Normandie and Millau are possible because of advances in material technology such as composites, advanced high-strength steels and concrete. Modern concretes have made this material attractive by adding micro silica and other compounds to greatly increase its strength. When designing main spans on the threshold of 2,000m (6,562ft) many more factors are now taken into consideration than in the past. These include live and dead loads of unprecedented magnitudes; severe environmental constraints including tidal currents of 4.5m/second, winds up to 8m/second and tectonic activities. At the moment, the cost of new materials is not competitive with conventional concrete and steel unless the entire life-cycle of a bridge is taken into account.

Bridge builders have perfected design, fabrication and construction techniques to a point where the challenges of building the world's longest suspension bridge could be met. Larger and more adventurous bridges are planned such as the Messina bridge linking Italy with Sicily and the Straits of Gibraltar, but this will not happen in the near future.

BRIDGE BUILDING

Above The Millau Viaduct spans the immense gorge of the River Tarn in France. The cable-stayed structure is currently the world's tallest road bridge with one mast reaching higher than the Eiffel Tower.

Right The fan shape of the Tatara Bridge's cables has been likened to that of a white bird spreading its wings. Since completion in 1999, the Sutong Bridge (2008) has surpassed it as the world's longest cable-stayed bridge.

EUROPE

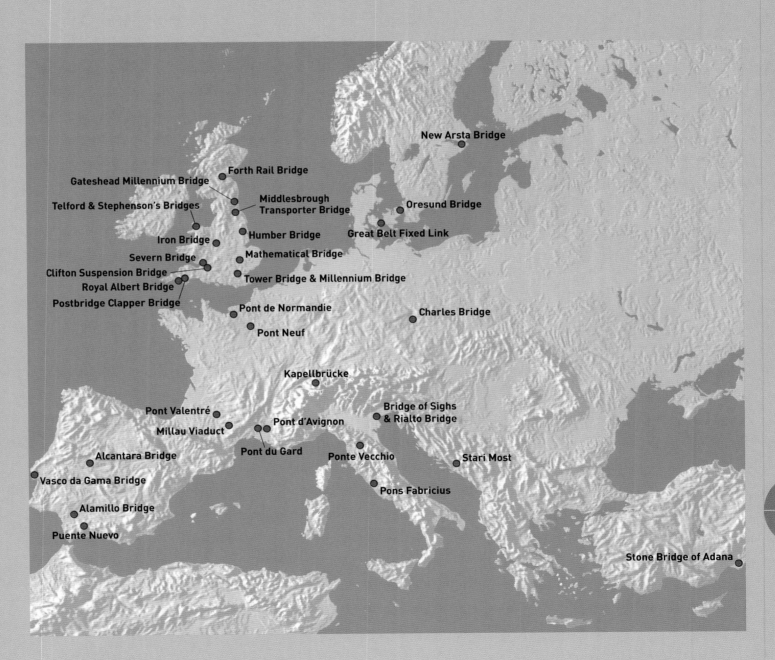

New Arsta Bridge

Forth Rail Bridge

Gateshead Millennium Bridge

Middlesbrough
Transporter Bridge

Oresund Bridge

Telford & Stephenson's Bridges

Humber Bridge

Great Belt Fixed Link

Iron Bridge

Mathematical Bridge

Severn Bridge

Clifton Suspension Bridge

Tower Bridge & Millennium Bridge

Royal Albert Bridge

Postbridge Clapper Bridge

Pont de Normandie

Charles Bridge

Pont Neuf

Kapellbrücke

Pont Valentré

Bridge of Sighs
& Rialto Bridge

Millau Viaduct

Pont d'Avignon

Alcantara Bridge

Pont du Gard

Ponte Vecchio

Stari Most

Vasco da Gama Bridge

Pons Fabricius

Alamillo Bridge

Puente Nuevo

Stone Bridge of Adana

Left The steps of the Rialto Bridge in Venice, Italy, are nearly always busy with tourists and shoppers.

STARI MOST

MOSTAR / **BOSNIA AND HERZEGOVINA**

An outstanding achievement by 16th-century Turkish architects, this bridge became a World Heritage Site in 2004 despite being entirely rebuilt after war damage in 1993. UNESCO recognised the reconstruction effort as a hugely significant symbol of peace and co-operation.

Name	Stari Most
Location	Mostar
Crosses	River Neretva
Type	Stone arch bridge
Function	Pedestrian bridge
Main span	27.3m (89.6ft)
Length	30m (98.4ft)
Height	19m (62.3ft)
Opened	1566, rebuilt 2004
Design	Mimar Hajruddin

THE ORIGINAL BRIDGE

Mostar, once part of the Ottoman Turkish Empire, was an important link between the Adriatic Sea and the interior of Bosnia. It had a medieval wooden bridge spanning its gorge so in 1557 Sultan Suleiman the Magnificent commissioned a replacement from architect Mimar Hajruddin. The design was so ingenious yet fragile-looking that it is said that Hayreddin prepared for death on the day it opened, or even dug his own grave, in case the bridge collapsed and he was executed.

DESTRUCTION

Flanked by two defensive towers, the slender limestone span was supported by abutments fixed to walls on the cliffs each side. It survived in a good state of preservation until the late 20th century, featuring on many tourist itineraries and even withstanding the weight of tanks passing over it during the Second World War.

However, as the conflict in former Yugoslavia erupted in the early 1990s, civil war broke out. In 1993 Croat forces shelled the bridge in an act of destruction for which they claimed military justification. However, it was generally condemned as cultural vandalism, an attack on Mostar's Islamic Turkish heritage and its multi-ethnic population where Croats, Bosnian Muslims and Serbs had once co-existed.

Right Shrouded in mystery over how its construction was achieved, the original Stari Most stood above the River Neretva for more than 400 years as a monument to Mostar's former Ottoman rulers.

STARI MOST

CO-OPERATION AND REBUILDING

International shock at the loss of the historic bridge led to an unprecedented co-operation after the war. At a cost of more than $13 million, the bridge and surrounding buildings were reconstructed, largely employing the same methods and materials as the original Turkish architects nearly 450 years before. The Italian structural engineers found the geometry of the curve of the bridge extremely complex to analyse; wider and shallower than a simple arc, it represented a way of spanning a high gorge without requiring a steep slope on each side of the roadway. Divers salvaged fallen stones from the river, and missing or unusable parts were replaced from the same quarry that had provided stone for the first bridge. Many of the blocks were fixed together using the original technique of metal reinforcement, with linking rods and brackets fitting into slots cut into the stone and the gaps filled with molten lead.

A NEW SYMBOL

International aid for the project, principally from Turkey, Italy, the Netherlands and France, was managed by the World Bank with technical assistance from UNESCO. The reconstruction was seen as a symbol of restored peace and ethnic harmony, though divisions in the local population remain and few Serbs have returned to the area.

TEST OF COURAGE

Nine young men revived the Mostar tradition of diving from the bridge to prove their courage at the 2004 opening ceremony, with a perilous leap into icy waters. Amir Pasic, who had led the restoration, emphasised the bridge's importance as a non-religious symbol open to everyone: '... something that is not a mosque or church, it's something for all people in general'. This significance, adding to its value as an historic structure, was also acknowledged by UNESCO who inscribed the 'new' bridge as a World Heritage Site in 2004 stating '... the symbolic power and meaning of the City of Mostar – as an exceptional and universal symbol of co-existence of communities from diverse cultural, ethnic and religious backgrounds – has been reinforced and strengthened'.

Mostar's Centre for Peace and Multi-ethnic Co-operation opened the year the reconstruction finished, with the aim of promoting the development of multi-ethnic societies in the area of former Yugoslavia. It awards an annual international Peace Prize to those contributing to bringing civilizations and cultures closer together.

Left Following the reconstruction of the bridge, the annual summer diving competition (held since 1968) was reinstated, although diving from the structure has been documented since the seventeenth century.

Right A view of the old bridge; after its destruction by artillery during the war in the 1990s, the bridge was rebuilt using original stone and traditional construction techniques.

CASTELVECCHIO BRIDGE, VERONA

Also known as Ponte Scaligero, this fortified bridge was another casualty of 20th-century warfare. At the time of its construction (around 1354–1356) the crossing included the longest arch span in Europe at 48.7m (160ft). Linked to the Castelvecchio fortress, it would have provided a safe escape route northwards for the tyrannical ruler Cangrande della Scala II, who feared a popular rebellion. Legend has it that the designer, Guglielmo Bevilacqua, attended the opening ceremony on horseback ready to flee for his life in case the bridge collapsed. While the arches are marble, the battlemented parapets and upper portions of the bridge are in red brick, as were the towers at each end. The bridge stood unscathed until the late 18th century, when French troops destroyed one tower, but the whole structure was blown up by retreating Nazi forces at the end of the Second World War in 1945, along with Verona's Roman bridge, the Ponte Pietra. Both were faithfully reconstructed during the 1950s.

CHARLES BRIDGE

PRAGUE / CZECH REPUBLIC

This outstanding example of medieval engineering was for more
than 400 years the sole link across the broad, swiftly flowing Vltava
(Moldau) River. Remodelled and repaired over the centuries, its styles
encompass Roman-style near-semicircular arches, Gothic gateways
and Baroque embellishments; all this against a magnificent backdrop
of the hilltop castle towering above.

PARLER'S CHALLENGE

No other medieval bridge spans such an extent of water as the Charles Bridge, which links Malá Strana (the Lesser Quarter) to Staré Mesto (the Old Town) in the Czech capital. The present structure replaced the Judith Bridge of 1172, swept away by floods in 1342, which had been only the second major stone medieval bridge to be built in central Europe after the 14-arch Steinerne Brücke (1146), which still stands at Regensburg in Germany. Charles IV (Karel IV), 11th king of Bohemia and Holy Roman Emperor, commissioned his 27-year-old German court architect Peter Parler, whose other works included St. Vitus Cathedral at Prague Castle, to provide a worthy replacement. Parler's challenge was to build another bridge that could cope both with heavy traffic loads and with the ever-present threat of flooding. The foundation stone was laid in 1357 and the work was completed 45 years later.

The 16 arches are shielded by wedge-shaped piers designed to guard against the destructive impact of winter ice. Egg yolks were reputedly mixed into the mortar as a strengthening agent. Yet the natural elements have continued to play havoc over the centuries. The bridge has been damaged on numerous occasions. There were further floods in 1432 and 1496, and in 1890 so much debris was washed against the bridge that two pillars collapsed, others were damaged and two statues were washed away. However, it survived a devastating flood in August 2002, the worst in the country for 500 years.

CONSTRUCTION AND RESTORATION

Up until 1870 this was known simply as the Stone Bridge, or Prague Bridge. It was initially conceived as a functional structure that could also be used for knightly tournaments and for many years its only decoration was a plain crucifix. Adornments with a more Baroque religious flavour came later: the famous statues began to be installed from the late 17th century.

The bridge is fortified on both sides by towers which served as look-out posts. On the Lesser Quarter side, a castellated arch links two bridge towers to form the entrance to the bridge, the smaller of which formed part of the original 12th-century Judith Bridge. Undoubtedly the most photographed tower, however, is on the Old Town side. It is rich in Gothic detailing, with sculptures of Charles IV, his son Wenceslas and St. Vitus. After an anti-Habsburg revolt, 27 rebels were executed in 1621 and their severed heads displayed here. This tower was badly damaged at the end of the Thirty Years' War in 1648 when Swedes occupied the west bank and tried to invade the Old Town – during which time the bridge was the scene of intense fighting.

A SHRINE ON THE BRIDGE

From 1683 approximately 30 Baroque statues of saints were erected on the bridge's balustrades, some by the leading Bohemian sculptors of the day including Matthias Braun and Maxmilian Brokoff. The best-known statue is of John of Nepomuk, a Czech martyr saint executed during the reign of Wenceslas IV by being thrown into the Vltava from the bridge; his image was placed here by Jesuits who ran a campaign to have him canonized, and it has been rubbed to a shine over the centuries by countless people touching it for good luck. Since 1965 there has been a programme of replacing the statues with replicas and transferring the much-weathered originals into the Lapidarium of the National Museum.

A TOURIST ATTRACTION

Operated as a toll bridge until 1805 and crossed by trams in the early decades of the 20th century, the 10-metre (32.8-foot) broad bridge has been free of traffic since 1950 and continues to be on almost every tourist itinerary. During the day it bustles with street musicians, souvenir stalls and street artists, and in the evening it becomes a popular gathering ground to view the castle, dramatically lit up against the dark sky. The delightful lamps, formerly lit by gas, were installed in 1866.

Name	Charles Bridge
Location	Prague
Crosses	Vltava River
Type	Stone arch bridge
Function	Pedestrian bridge
Length	515m (1,692ft)
Opened	1402
Design	Peter Parler

Left Four bridges across the Vltava: (from the foreground) Manesuv Bridge, Charles Bridge, Legii Bridge and the Jiraskuv Bridge. There are at least four other crossings in the centre of Prague alone.

Right For centuries the Charles Bridge was the only means of crossing the Vltava. Spanning half a kilometre across the river, the bridge helped to establish the city as a trade route between eastern and western Europe.

GREAT BELT FIXED LINK

ZEALAND AND SPROGØ / **DENMARK**

The strait known as the Great Belt, or Storebælt, is linked by the Great Belt Fixed Link, an ambitious road and rail route between the two largest Danish islands. After more than 50 years of planning and discussion, it became the largest construction project in Danish history.

A MAMMOTH PROJECT

The scheme to build the Great Belt Fixed Link finally got the go-ahead in 1986 with work beginning two years later. Replacing a ferry journey that took over an hour with a crossing that can be done in ten minutes, the Link forms part of a project that provides a land route through the most populous part of Denmark. In its entirety, the 18-kilometre (11-mile) route consists of two sections joining Zealand – the largest Danish island and which includes the capital Copenhagen – to Nybørg on the island of Funen, of which the largest settlement is Odense. The two sections meet at the small islet of Sprogø in the middle of the Great Belt strait. Sprogø itself quadrupled in size through land reclamation alone. Along the eastern part road traffic uses the Eastern Bridge, while trains take the Eastern Tunnel. The Western Bridge combines road and rail traffic. Tolls are levied for road traffic and for trains.

THE EASTERN LINK

The name Great Belt is often used to refer only to the Eastern Bridge. This has one of the world's longest main spans of any suspension bridge at 1,624m (5,328ft) and its pylons are the tallest solid structures in Denmark at 254m (833ft). The approach viaducts rise gently over 13 spans to give the main deck some 65m (213ft) of clearance, required by the volume of heavy shipping moving between the Baltic and the North Sea. In an innovative refinement of previous suspension bridge designs, the two cables are tensioned by being fixed to offshore anchor blocks rather than to points on dry land. To provide a firm foundation in the clay seabed under some 10m (32.8ft) of water, prefabricated reinforced concrete caissons were sunk into position to support the legs and cross beam of the anchor blocks.

Trains use the two tunnel tubes of the Eastern Tunnel (Østtunnelen), 8km (5 miles) long and 7.7m (25ft) in diameter. Between the two main tunnels are 31 connecting tunnels at regular intervals of 250m (820ft), for housing equipment and for use as emergency escape routes.

THE WEST BRIDGE

The prefabricated concrete Great Belt West Bridge (Vestbroen) is a box girder construction of over 6.6km (4.1 miles), comprising two adjacent bridges with separate decks to carry rail and motorway traffic. It consists of 63 sections, supported by 62 pillars, and sharing foundations beneath the water. Its 324 huge prefabricated parts were lifted into place by 'Svanen', ('the swan') a purpose-made self-powered floating crane.

TIME SAVER

The opening of the link trebled road traffic within its first eight years, and journey time by car was reduced from 90 minutes to less than 15 minutes. Part of the reason for this is the increase in capacity, compared to the ferry. The short journey time by road or rail between the cities of Copenhagen and Odense has meant that domestic flights between those two points now no longer operate. Uninterrupted rail travel is now possible from Copenhagen to mainland Europe and the United Kingdom.

Name	Great Belt East Bridge
Location	Between Zealand and islet of Sprogø
Crosses	Great Belt
Type	Suspension bridge
Function	Road bridge
Main span	1,624m (5,328ft)
Length	6,790m (22,277ft)
Clearance	65m (213ft)
Opened	1998
Design	Dissing and Weitling

Name	Great Belt West Bridge
Location	Between islet of Sprogø and Knudshoved
Crosses	Great Belt
Type	Box girder bridge
Function	Road and rail bridge
Length	6,611m (21,690ft)
Clearance	18m (59ft)
Opened	1994
Design	Højgaard & Schultz

53

Left The largest construction project in Danish history, the Eastern Great Belt link combines a box girder bridge with a suspension bridge that boasts the third longest main span in the world at 1.6km (1 mile).

ORESUND BRIDGE

ORESUND STRAIT / **DENMARK AND SWEDEN**

No other border crossing bridge is on the scale of this sinuous structure, Europe's longest combined road and rail bridge, which gracefully curves its way from the Swedish city of Malmø to descend into a tunnel on the artificial, unpopulated island of Peberholm.

CAPITAL CONNECTION

This co-operative venture between Denmark and Sweden has dramatically redrawn the map of this southern corner of Scandinavia, and has provided a huge boost to the region. It connects the metropolitan areas of the Oresund Region, as well as the cities of Copenhagen in Denmark and Malmø in Sweden. Starting from the Swedish shore, the bridge comprises 49 approach spans of uniform design with spans between 120 and 140m (460 and 1,608ft), and a 490-metre central span of harp-like cable stays. It carries two railway lines below a four-

lane motorway across the Oresund Strait, to end at the island of Peberholm, created from material dredged from the sea bed during construction of the piers and the 4-km (2.5 mile) Drogden Tunnel. From here the motorway and railway descend and run parallel at the same level through the tunnel to Zealand, the largest Danish island. The proximity to Copenhagen's new airport meant a bridge here was not practicable. When completed in 1999 the bridge broke records for the highest free-standing pylons ever built for a bridge – 204m (668ft). In fact, the design process had to counter the

Right The world's longest border crossing bridge, the Oresund Bridge is also Europe's longest combined road and rail bridge. While early use of the bridge was lower than expected, 25 million people a year now cross by car or train.

Name	Oresund Bridge
Location	Sweden and Denmark
Crosses	Oresund Strait
Type	Cable-stayed bridge
Function	Road and rail bridge
Main span	490m (1,608ft)
Length	7.8km (4.9 miles)
Clearance	57m (187ft)
Opened	2000
Design	Georg Rotne

anticipated effects of perspective caused by the sheer height; it may have appeared that a perfectly vertical structure was leaning inwards if viewed from the bridge deck level.

NEW WAYS OF WORKING

Since the opening of the bridge and tunnel, many Danes have moved to Sweden, where property prices are lower, and commuted from there, while numerous Swedes have taken advantage of higher wages and better job opportunities by finding work in Denmark. Among many companies to relocate to the area are Daimler-Chrysler

Left Few bridges link two nations separated by sea; the elegant grace of the Oresund Bridge stretches 7.8km (4.9 miles) across the Strait that shares its name and links Denmark and Sweden.

corporation, which moved its Scandinavian operation to new headquarters near the bridge. The link takes high-speed trains that can travel in excess of 200kph (124mph), and has made non-stop rail travel feasible from Norway to Spain or Greece. Meanwhile the new islet of Peberholm has flourished as an undisturbed nature haven, home to more than 450 different types of plants as well as the endangered green toad, birds such as the rare avocet and the little tern, and unusual spiders and insects.

Malmø and Copenhagen have also integrated their transport systems, and colleges in the region have formed a 'networked university'. The Mayor of Malmø, Ilmar Reepalu, said 'Mental bridges are already being built, because of the physical bridge.'

CONNECTING CONTINENTS: SPANNING THE BOSPHORUS

While the Oresundsbron joins two countries divided by sea, the two Bosphorus Bridges in Istanbul connect two continents, Europe and Asia, and stand about 5km (3.1 miles) apart. Both are motorway bridges designed by Freeman Fox & Partners. The First Bosphorus Bridge is a gravity-anchored suspension bridge with steel pylons. Its deck hangs on zigzag cables and has a 64-metre (210-foot) clearance above the water – with a main span of 1,074m (3,524ft) the structure was the largest of its kind outside the US when opened in 1973. The Second Bosphorus Bridge, also known as the Fatih Sultan Mehmet Bridge, is similar but slightly longer at 1,090m (3,576ft), with its deck hanging on traditional vertical cables.

Below Approximately, 180,000 cars cross the Bosphorus between the two continents each day. No pedestrians can use the bridge but an intercontinental marathon passes over it once a year.

PONT NEUF

PARIS / FRANCE

The Pont Neuf, meaning the 'new bridge' is anything but what its title suggests, being the oldest surviving bridge across the Seine in Paris. The city's most beautiful span, Parisians have cherished it as a place for socialising ever since its inauguration more than 400 years ago.

A BRIDGE FOR THE PEOPLE

In the mid 16th century, Paris had just two bridges, both of which were rickety and overcrowded. Accordingly King Henri III ordered the building of this spacious 22-metre (72.2-foot) wide stone bridge, spanning the river via the western end of the Île de la Cité, the island in the middle of the Seine, at the heart of medieval Paris. It was the first bridge in the French capital to be built without houses on it, and the first equipped with pavements for pedestrians, who could meet, talk and walk at leisure without interference from horses and carts. In 1578 Henri III laid the first stone, but war intervened and the structure was not completed until 29 years later.

In 1607 the Pont Neuf acquired its name from Henry IV when he officially opened it. An equestrian statue of the monarch was erected at the centre of the bridge after the king's death. This was removed and melted down during the French Revolution, but the original cast had survived, allowing an exact replica to be made in 1818 and placed in position.

KEY FEATURES

The bridge comprises two parts either side of the Île de la Cité, of five and seven spans respectively. Its arch construction follows the Roman pattern that was the norm for this period in bridge building. A large-scale restoration project was carried out over 13 years and completed in 2007, the year of its 400th anniversary, but there has never been a fundamental alteration to the structure. It still retains the original wooden pilings that support the foundations. A plaque by steps from the bridge to the Île de la Cité marks the execution of Jacques de Molay, the last Grand Master of the Knights Templar burned at the stake on the island on 18 March, 1314.

INSPIRATION

The bridge has inspired many artists. Claude Monet painted a view in 1872 with steam rising from a vessel on the Seine and people with umbrellas walking across in the rain. Another impressionist, Camille Pissarro, used it as a subject for several of his works, probably painted from his apartment on the Île de la Cité. The broad walkways under the arches at the shore ends of the bridge have also provided shelter to the homeless over the centuries; the bridge provided the backdrop for the 1991 film *Les Amants de Pont Neuf* which revolves around a romance between two young vagrants who live on and around the bridge while it is closed for restoration. Director Leos Carax's permit to film on the bridge expired before he had finished, and the film had to be completed on a full-scale replica constructed on a lake in the South of France, making this one of the most expensive French films ever made.

Left For many years the widest bridge in Paris, the Pont Neuf's structure has never been altered, and the original wooden pilings supporting the foundations are still in place beneath the surface of the Seine.

Right Composed of twelve separate arches on either side of Île de la Cité, the wide arches of the Pont Neuf have provided a haven for the destitute of Paris for centuries.

Name	Pont Neuf
Location	Paris
Crosses	River Seine
Type	Stone arch bridge
Function	Road and pedestrian bridge
Span lengths	9 to 16.4m (29.5 to 53.8ft)
Length	232m (761ft)
Opened	1607

THE MILLAU VIADUCT

MILLAU / **FRANCE**

Elegantly resolving an infamous bottleneck in the French highway network, the Millau Viaduct spans the immense gorge of the River Tarn between two high limestone plateaus or *causses*, bypassing the town of Millau. Its opening in 2004 finally completed the A75 as a continuous high-speed autoroute bisecting France from north to south between Paris and Barcelona.

THE TALLEST ROAD BRIDGE
Despite its setting within the sensitive environment of the Grands Causses Regional Natural Park, the bridge, designed by Norman Foster and Michel Virlogeux has been widely applauded for its beauty, becoming a tourist attraction in its own right and a symbol for the region.

The cable-stayed, masted structure is currently the world's tallest road bridge, with one mast reaching 343m (1,125ft), higher even than France's best-known iconic structure, the Eiffel Tower. Its bridge deck – the world's longest cable-stayed roadway at

2,460m (8,071ft) long – is suspended 270m (886ft) above the River Tarn at its highest point and follows a gentle curve with a 20-km (12.4-mile) radius. The eight spans are supported by seven concrete pillars; the six central spans each measure 342m (1,063ft) with two outer spans measuring 204m (669ft).

SITTING ON CLOUDS
To allow the deck to expand and contract with temperature variations, each column divides into two narrower, more flexible columns below. This gives a strikingly slender silhouette which minimises the visual impact on the landscape. At the

Left The viaduct spans the valley of the River Tarn close to the town of Millau. Each of the pylons are supported by shafts (5m (16ft) in circumference) driven to a depth of 15m (49ft) and.

inauguration in 2004, the architect Norman Foster said that he intended the bridge to be designed to have the 'delicacy of a butterfly...the pillars had to look almost organic, like they had grown from the earth'. When the characteristic morning mists form in the Tarn valley, it can appear that the bridge is sitting on clouds.

A DELICATE ASSEMBLY

After ten years of planning for the challenges of the high winds and complex geology of the area, the Anglo-French project began construction in October 2001. The work cost 394 million euros, financed privately by the French construction firm Eiffage which incorporates the original firm that built the Eiffel Tower. In return, the firm retained the right to collect bridge tolls for 75 years. During a delicate assembly process, sections of the decks were lifted slightly and slid out from the pylons over further temporary pylons by satellite-guided hydraulic rams at speeds of just 15cm (5.9 inches) a minute. The masts were then transported over the new sections of

deck and put up on top of the pylons, before the temporary pylons were removed.

TOURIST TRAFFIC

The first traffic crossed the bridge in December 2004 following an inauguration by French President Jacques Chirac. The speed limit of 130kph (91mph) was soon reduced to 110kph (68.4mph) to allow for motorists who slowed their vehicles in order to take photographs as they crossed.

Before the bridge was completed, traffic had to cross the River Tarn at a bridge in Millau at the bottom of the valley, a congestion point resulting in huge queues, delays and pollution during the holiday season in July and August. Now, as a result of the new bridge, Millau is reportedly enjoying an economic boom, with two industrial zones, La Cavalerie to the south, and Sévérac-le-Château to the north, benefitting. Meanwhile tourists bound for southern France and Spain can follow a direct and toll-free route (apart from the bridge itself) for 340km (211 miles) across the Massif Central.

Name	Millau Viaduct
Location	Millau, France
Crosses	River Tarn valley
Type	Cable-stayed bridge
Function	Road bridge
Longest span	342m (1,122ft)
Length	2,460m (8,071ft)
Clearance	270 metres (886ft)
Opened	2004
Design	Norman Foster and Michel Virlogeux

Right The Millau Viaduct is the tallest vehicular bridge in the world and as a result frequently sits above the cloudline; indeed, admirers have labelled it the motorway in the clouds.

THE WORLD'S HIGHEST BRIDGES

A boardwalk suspended 321m (1,053ft) above the Arkansas river, the world's highest bridge is currently the Royal Gorge Bridge, near Cañon City, Colorado. It was built as a tourist attraction in 1929 and was not designed for use by transportation. Another high-flying American attraction nearby, is the horseshoe-shaped glass walkway of the Grand Canyon Skywalk. At 1,200 metres (3,937 feet) above the floor of the canyon its position exceeds that of many skyscrapers though this is not technically a bridge.

Millau Viaduct's record for the world's highest vehicular bridge deck is likely to be soon overtaken by the Chenab Bridge on the Kashmir Railway, northern India, 359 metres above the river. The railway, a 290-km (180-mile) extension of the Indian Railway network, passes through the Himalayan foothills and is being engineered to withstand earthquakes and extreme winters. Its gentle 1% gradient will be achieved through a series of immense tunnels, up to 11km (6.8 miles) long, and bridges, with only a fifth of the route being at the original ground level. It is scheduled for completion in 2009.

Above The Royal Gorge Bridge was built purely as a tourist attraction and not for rail or road use (the railroad runs along the base of the gorge). At 321m above the Arkansas River, it is the world's highest bridge.

PONT DE NORMANDIE

NORMANDY / FRANCE

The soaring slenderness of the Pont de Normandie drew the attention of the French public and awakened a new national interest in innovative bridge-building. Its designer, Michel Virlogeux, went on to collaborate with Foster and Partners on the Millau Viaduct.

PONT DE NORMANDIE

CABLE-STAYED RECORD

At the time of its completion in 1995, the Pont de Normandie was the world's longest cable-stayed bridge, overtaking the previous record-holder, the Skarnsundet Bridge in Norway and stretches a full 42 per cent further. This type of design was the best technological and economic solution to the problem of creating a bridge that gave access to heavy shipping in a large area characterised by unstable river sediments, with no natural anchorage points, and high winds. The bridge relieves traffic on the Tancarville Bridge (1959), near Le Havre, and improves access to and from western France. The four-lane roadway rises markedly to cross 52m (170.6ft) above the high-tide level in a single span, and the inverted Y-shaped

Right The roadway begins its journey across the Seine. The cable-stayed design was chosen because it was both cheaper and more resistant to high winds than a suspension bridge.

pylons are so high and far apart that the curvature of the Earth means that they are 2cm (0.8 inches) further apart at the top than at the base.

USING DAMPERS

The central section of the main span of the deck is made of steel for lightness and strength. This posed a challenge during construction, as its two halves were launched out from the pylons on each side and for a time hung unsupported and vulnerable to gusts of wind. Anchoring them to the bank with cables would have proved a hazard to shipping, so 50-tonne counterweights were included on each deck, capable of moving in any direction to damp down any vibrations. These 'tuned mass dampers' proved a success, although experimental at the time. The aerofoil-type deck profile received extensive testing in wind tunnels to prove its stability. Each staying cable is designed so that it can be

removed without interfering with the flow of traffic, and to prevent the cables from striking against each other, cross-cables known as damping ropes were added to reduce and counteract any movement.

A QUESTION OF AESTHETICS

Construction took seven years and attracted increasing attention. Designer Michel Virlogeux recalled in an interview with *The New Civil Engineer* magazine in 2005 that there had been little interest during the planning of the bridge, but as the structure went up, 'suddenly, everyone had something to say about it'. Virlogeux, an engineer by training, believes that aesthetics should be as central to the process of bridge design as they were in the 18th and 19th centuries. He dislikes over-reliance on computerised calculations, believing that they stifle creativity, by making complex solutions as easy to calculate as elegantly simple ones.

Name	Pont de Normandie
Location	Normandy, France
Crosses	River Seine
Type	Cable-stayed bridge
Function	Road bridge
Span	856m (2,808ft)
Length	2,141m (7,024ft)
Height	215m (705ft)
Clearance	52m (171ft)
Opened	1995
Design	Michel Virlogeux

Far Right At the time of construction the 856m (0.53 mile) main span was the longest in the world. However, this record has since been beaten by the Tatara Bridge (1999, see page 188) and the Sutong Bridge (2008), also in Japan.

CABLE-STAYED BRIDGES IN SOUTH AMERICA

Concrete and steel cable-stayed bridge designs have a strikingly modern appearance and are often used because, compared to suspension bridges, they are relatively lightweight and less costly to construct. Architect Michel Virlogeux ranks the General Rafael Urdaneta bridge (also known as the Lake Maracaibo Bridge) in Venezuela, opened in 1962, as among the world's greatest bridges, along with the Golden Gate, the Forth and the Brooklyn Bridges. It consists of five main spans each of 253m (771ft) and six towers 92m (302ft) tall, which have become a symbol of Venezuelan national pride, and are illuminated in changing colours at night by the most extensive architectural lighting project in South America. The bridge crosses the narrowest part of Lake Maracaibo, one of the world's oldest lakes, sparing travellers a ferry journey that used to take two hours.

In neighbouring Colombia, the César Gaviria Trujillo Viaduct, opened in 1997, links the cities of Pereira and Dosquebradas, spanning a deep river valley with a 440-metre viaduct with a central span of 211m (692ft) and two pylons with an elongated diamond shape. The viaduct reduces traffic congestion in the two cities and has had a significant effect on the local economy through reduced journey times. It was built by a Brazilian and German joint venture, with assistance from French and Portuguese companies.

Right Riccardo Morandi's version of the General Rafael Urdaneta bridge was the only concrete design put forward in the initial design competition to build the structure.

PONT DU GARD

VERS-PONT-DU-GARD NEAR REMOULINS / **FRANCE**

Surviving almost intact after two millennia, the Pont du Gard, the most celebrated aqueduct surviving from the Roman world, combines the aesthetics of classical architecture with remarkable engineering and bridge-building prowess.

CIVILIZED ROMAN LIFE

It was the crowning achievement of an ambitious aqueduct thought to have been completed around AD60, a water-supply scheme leading some 50 kilometres (31 miles) from a spring by the Eure in Uzès to the water tower (Castellum) in the city of Nîmes, one of the greatest cities of Gaul and a Roman colony from AD40.

With its completion, the aqueduct supplied some 20,000 cubic metres each day, providing Nîmes with all the convenience and decorative features that ensured a civilised Roman life, after the city's spring proved no longer adequate for the purpose. Water ran underground for most of the aqueduct's length, through a 1.2-m (3.9-ft) wide channel which had an average height of 1.8m (6ft), and along the entire distance

the drop was just 71m (233ft) (equating to an incline of 34cm per km or 1ft per mile). The intervening area of scrubland and forest would have required a painstakingly careful survey to ensure gravity would do the work effectively. An application of lime and water was added to the stone channel to keep parasites and vegetation at bay.

THREE TIERS

The solution to spanning the steep-sided valley of the River Gardon was to build in three tiers to convey the water channel along the top tier, 47m (154ft) above the river. Wide arches and breakwaters at the footings enable the aqueduct to withstand flood surges. Mortar was used only at the top level, and large slabs sealed the channel. The spans of the bottom and middle arches range from 15.75 to 21.5m (51.7 to 70.5ft).

Right By transporting plentiful water from the Eure, the aqueduct brought fountains, spas and sewage networks to Nîmes, firmly establishing it as one of the greatest cities in Gaul.

The estimated 21,000 cubic metres of honey-coloured stone was locally sourced, most of it from a quarry just 600 metres upstream. On the second tier, numerous stones protrude from the structure. These are chiselled-off remains of the blocks used to support lifting apparatus during building. There are six arches on the bottom tier and 11 on the middle. The top tier now has 35 arches, but originally consisted of 47; 12 were removed in the medieval period. In 1743 the bridge was adapted, and bore a road on top of its first tier, which was doubled in width. Since then, the structure has been restored on various occasions.

Left The aqueduct still bears the scars of its construction, with protruding scaffolding supports and ridges on the piers forming the last traces of the wooden frames.

THE HERITAGE AQUEDUCT

The Pont du Gard became a UNESCO World Heritage Site in 1985 and the left bank hosts an information centre and exhibition hall which has been carefully designed and positioned so as not to detract from the historic landmark. The exhibition shows how water was used to enrich the civilised lifestyle of the Romans – wealthy households had their own piped supply, public baths were constructed, fountains graced public areas and water powered industry. It also deals with the geological challenges that were overcome during the construction of the aqueduct.

The arches are uncommonly broad for a Roman building: the ratio between pier and span, normally 1:3, is here nearly 1:5. There is no record of the builders and engineers who constructed the Pont du Gard. The only inscription on the structure is on a pile at the bottom: 'mens totum corium', denoting simply that the aqueduct has been measured. People are no longer allowed onto the Pont itself but it is possible to walk over the bridge that runs alongside it at the same level as the first tier of arches.

Name	Pont du Gard
Location	Vers-Pont-du-Gard
Type	Stone aqueduct
Height	47.4m (156ft)
Total length	(Top tier) 275m (902ft)
Maximum span	24.4m (80ft)
Completed	c AD60

SEGOVIA AND OTHER ROMAN AQUEDUCTS

Another great Roman aqueduct was built to convey water 15 kilometres from the Guadarrama mountains to the city of Segovia in central Spain. For most of its length, the Segovia Aqueduct consisted of underground channels, but its final section required bridging the valley with a huge arched structure; this was an opportunity for the city to create a grand architectural statement of its prosperity. At 800m (2,625ft), it is longer than the Pont du Gard, and includes a remarkably slender double row of arches that reach 36m (118ft) in height and the piers of which are just 2.4m (8ft) across at their base. The construction bore an inscription of bronze letters attached with lead pegs, which were prised off in medieval times by someone who recognised the value of the material. The remaining peg holes indicated what the inscription said – telling us that work was carried out in AD98 under Emperor Trajan. However, the original structure is thought to have been erected during the reign of Domitian (AD81–96), whose name was removed from monuments after he was assassinated: A niche above the inscription that now contains a figure of the Madonna is thought to have held his statue.

There were 11 aqueducts in ancient Rome, providing for a city that exceeded a million inhabitants more than a cubic metre of water per person each day, and supplying great amounts for bath houses. The aqueducts were constructed between 312BC and AD226, the first being the Aqua Appia and the longest the Anio Novus (95km (59 miles)). Water ran along channels for most of the length of the aqueducts at a shallow gradient of 1:200 or less, taking a contouring route and requiring the construction of arches to bear the conduits for the final sections into the city; several fragments of these arched sections survive. The water flowed into huge cisterns, and then along lead pipes. Most of the population took their water from public fountains, but some privileged individuals could afford to have it piped into their homes.

Another substantial arched structure built to convey a Roman aqueduct is to be found on the sandy shores of the Mediterranean near Caesarea in Israel. The aqueduct ran 9km (5.6 miles) from springs at the base of Mount Carmel to the city. The date of construction is not known but an inscription records that construction was carried out during the reign of Hadrian (AD117–138). However, this is now thought to have been when the second channel was added. Caesarea was founded by Herod the Great in 22BC, but his extensive building work was described in detail by Josephus who said nothing about the aqueduct itself.

Left The aqueduct at Segovia brought water from Spring Fuenfría, situated in the nearby mountains some 17km (10.6 miles) from La Acebeda.

PONT D'AVIGNON

AVIGNON / **FRANCE**

Also known as the Pont St-Bénézet, the Pont d'Avignon was among the first great stone bridges of the early medieval period, when western Europe was rediscovering how to build in stone on a scale not seen since the Roman Empire. Its incomplete remains, with their slender elliptical arches, recall an achievement so impressive that it appears to be divinely inspired.

A TURBULENT RIVER
The Rhône has always been known for its turbulent floods and since Roman times its ferries have always offered a hazardous form of transportation. The construction of a bridge at Avignon in the 12th century provided a relatively safe crossing of the river, the first for some 270km (168 miles) between Lyon and the Mediterranean. With the opening of the bridge, Avignon's fortunes rose as a centre for merchants and through collecting tolls, to the point where the French-born Pope Clement V moved his base there from Rome in 1309 (it would remain

the Papal centre until 1377). Many of the cardinals serving the Pope built residences across the bridge to escape the pollution of the city, and would have used the bridge to cross to the Papal Palace.

THE TALE OF ST. BÉNÉZET
The inspiration for the bridge seems to have come from a young man called Bénézet, who somehow won support for his project from wealthy sponsors. He died in 1184, just before the bridge was completed, and he was interred on the bridge itself in a small chapel. Not long afterwards

Right One of the most iconic bridges in France, the Pont d'Avignon has not been used as a river crossing since 1668, when it was badly damaged by floods.

the legend of St. Bénézet arose. The story, believed to have been spread by monks to help to raise money from the faithful in the surrounding countryside, was that Bénézet ('little Benedict') a young shepherd of slight build, heard a voice commanding him to build a bridge over the Rhône at Avignon. An angel guided him to the town where he was received with scorn, but he impressed the townsfolk by picking up an enormously heavy stone and carrying it to the river. Convinced that it was God's will, the population rallied round to construct the bridge.

Maintaining the bridge proved costly. Much of it was destroyed in a siege in 1226, and it was rebuilt around 1350. In subsequent centuries its condition deteriorated, with arch collapses following flooding in 1603 and 1605. The townsfolk resorted to a combination of a ferry to a mid-stream island, and rickety wooden steps and spans across the gaps.

OVER OR UNDER?
Today the bridge is associated with the lines of the French song often taught to schoolchildren, celebrating folk dancers circling round on (*sur*) the bridge:

> Sur le pont d'Avignon
> L'on y danse, l'on y danse
> Sur le pont d'Avignon
> L'on y danse tous en rond

The wording is curious, since the bridge is clearly too narrow for a circle dance. The explanation lies in the original words of the song, from the 16th century, which started *Sus (modern French: sous) le pont*: under the bridge. People would probably have danced beneath the bridge where it crossed an island, a popular recreation spot. The more modern version was popularised by two French operettas of 1853 and 1876, which used the changed and misleading wording.

BRIDGE-BUILDING BROTHERHOODS
In 12th- and 13th-century Europe religious associations known as the *Fratres Pontifeces*, or Bridge-Building Brotherhoods, were established to build structures across France. Assisting travellers, particularly pilgrims, was considered a religious duty, and helping to create a bridge was a very visible way of fulfilling it. The Brotherhoods were not solely monastic orders; they could include noblemen, who provided most of the money, the craftsmen who did the construction work, and women. St. Bénézet's wealthy sponsors must have formed the core of the Avignon Brotherhood, though little detail is known about them. Their decision must have been as commercially astute as it was religiously motivated, as the bridge provided the city with tolls on the only fixed crossing of the Rhône south of Lyon, as well as facilitating a key pilgrimage route from northern and central Europe to Santiago de Compostela in northwest Spain. In that sense it must have represented a better financial deal than funding one of the great cathedrals also being constructed at the time. As well as bridge-building, the associations provided lodgings for pilgrims and raised funds for the destitute.

Right After Arles lost its Roman bridge, the Pont d'Avignon became the only bridge to cross the Rhone between Lyon and the Mediterranean; the resulting trade saw Avignon flourish in the 14th century.

Name	Pont d'Avignon
Location	Avignon
Crosses	River Rhône
Type	Stone arch bridge
Function	Road and pedestrian bridge
Spans	22 arches of 30.8 to 33.5m (101 to 110ft)
Length	Originally 920m (3018ft)
Completed	1185

THE STONE BRIDGE, REGENSBURG
Built between 1135 and 1146, Regensburg's Steinerne Brücke (Stone Bridge) is another of the early European Medieval constructions associated with a religious brotherhood. Germanic knights bound on Crusades for the Holy Land used it to cross the Danube, and it also provided a trade route to places as far apart as Paris, Venice and Novgorod in Russia. Only a third the length of the Avignon bridge, with 14 arches spanning between 10.5 and 16.7m (34 and 55ft), the Regensburg bridge was for 800 years the city's only bridge over the Danube. Its piers are set on artificial islands, so close together that they create fierce rapids as water passes between the arches.

PONT VALENTRÉ

CAHORS / FRANCE

Familiar to many from a range of Cahors' wine labels, this distinctive three-towered bridge is the best-surviving fortified bridge from the medieval period in France. In its heyday, it bristled with state-of-the-art defensive devices.

PONT VALENTRÉ

Name	Pont Valentré
Location	Cahors
Crosses	River Lot
Type	Stone arch fortified bridge
Function	Road and pedestrian bridge
Main span	Six arches of 16.5m (54ft)
Length	138m (453ft)
Clearance	8.7m (28.5ft)
Height	40m (131ft)
Completed	1378

FORTIFIED STRUCTURE

At the time it was built, the Pont Valentré would have been in an isolated position, some way from the old town and guarding its western approaches across the River Lot. The piers for the six arches are built onto bedrock and have long cutwaters, that help to protect the piers themselves, extending upwater: the walls of the piers rise straight up to the castellated parapets, giving the structure a strong, vertical look. It has three square towers, one towards each end and

one serving as a look-out post in the middle. There were additionally fortified entrances at each bank. Although the first stone was formally laid in 1308, it is not clear when the bridge was completed. It was in use from about 1350 although the final work seems to have continued until 1378.

IMPERVIOUS TO ATTACK

The first storey of each tower was reached by external stairways, with timber stairways inside leading to the two upper floors. The end towers featured drawbridges and heavy doors, narrow slits for firing arrows and bolts from the first and second floors and machiolations – projecting parapets with gaps in the floor for throwing missiles down on attackers – on the third floor, along with covered loopholes for longer-range firing. Considering that there were also earthworks and fortifications in front of the towers, and that the old town of Cahors was enclosed on almost all sides by a loop in the river, an attack would have been a formidable undertaking.

THE DEVIL'S WORK

Unlike the Pont d'Avignon and its associations with St. Bénézet (see page 72), a legend concerning the Cahors bridge involves the work of the Devil. The unknown architect, struggling with the task of building the bridge, made a pact with Satan. In return for the architect's soul, Satan would help him to complete the bridge and obey his every order. When the bridge was almost finished, realising that his soul was in peril, the architect ordered the Devil to carry water in a sieve which proved beyond even him; thwarted, he vowed revenge. It is said that the stonemasons never were able to complete the top of the central tower on the bridge. Every morning when they arrived to start work, they found that a stone had been pulled out during the night.

The architect who carried out the restorations between 1867–1879, Paul Goût, had a small carving of a devil placed on the central tower where the stone was missing as a reminder of the legend.

Above and Right According to local legend, the Devil took a hand in building the Pont Valentré, a tale commemorated in the 19th-century restoration works, which included a carving of the devil trying but failing to remove a cornerstone of the bridge.

FORTIFIED BRIDGES

A bridge would often be one of the main entrances to a medieval town or city, linking to a gate in its walls and forming an important part of its defences. During the great castle-building period of the 13th and 14th centuries, many of Europe's strategically important bridges, along with castles, town walls and gates, were built or fortified with impressive-looking defensive devices such as arrow-slits, machiolations (see above) and castellated parapets. Along with the Valentré bridge, the best surviving examples are at Tournai (Belgium), Orthez in southwest France, Toledo (Spain) and Verona (Italy).

Monnow Bridge in Monmouth, on the Welsh-English border, is the only remaining medieval fortified river bridge in Britain with a gatehouse on it. The stone bridge was constructed around 1270, on the site of a previous wooden bridge of about 1180; timbers from this were discovered during a flood prevention scheme in 1989 and were dated using tree-ring analysis. The gatehouse was not an original feature, but added as part of improvements to the town defences that started around 1300. Like most medieval stone buildings, it would probably have been plastered and whitewashed. In the 18th century the gatehouse, no longer needed for defensive purposes, was converted into a dwelling, with its castellated parapet converted into solid walls and the roof raised.

Right The Monnow Bridge is located at the confluence of the Wye and Monnow Rivers in Monmouthshire. Alongside the Pont Valentré it is one of the best known medieval fortified bridges in Europe.

PONS FABRICIUS

ROME / **ITALY**

The oldest bridge in Rome still in use, the Pons Fabricius, is named after the Commissioner for Roads when it was built. It is also known as Quattro Capi after the four-headed figure that now stands at its east end.

A ROMAN CROSSING

There are records of eight ancient Roman bridges built over the Tiber: six survive, of which this and the Ponte Sant'Angelo retain the most substantially Roman characteristics. The Pons Fabricius was a public bridge connecting the Theatre of Marcellus with Tiber Island, which was frequented in Roman times by those seeking cures for a range of ailments at the Temple of Aesculapius. It was the first bridge to the island and the improved access seems to have been associated with a surge in popularity of the temple cult. The sick were treated on the island and a century later there are accounts of elderly and infirm slaves being abandoned there, presumably to the care of the sanctuary staff. After the Pons Fabricius was completed Lucius Cestius, a former governor of Rome, started work on another bridge, the Pons Cestius, connecting the far side of the island to the banks. This was completed in 36BC. Roman dignitaries often sponsored public works of this kind, along with entertainments such as circus games and gladiatorial contests, in order to boost their popularity among the citizens and gain prestige over their rivals.

STORIES OF CONSTRUCTION

The Roman historian Dio Cassius recorded that the Pons Fabricius was built in 62BC,

replacing a wooden bridge of 192BC that was destroyed by fire. Built originally of the porous rock peperino tufa and faced mainly with travertine (a local limestone), this replacement is 5.5m (18ft) wide and has two particularly long spans for a bridge of this antiquity, with a smaller central arch to provide extra channels for flood waters, and two small arches (now hidden) in the abutments. In 1679, Pope Innocent XI replaced the parapet. According to legend, the four-headed pilaster at the east end represents four architects hired by Pope Sixtus V to restore the bridge in the late 16th century, who were beheaded for constantly quarrelling with each other.

The bridge has been refaced in brick and its deck and parapets replaced, but otherwise the Roman structure is essentially intact, and the original tufa can be seen in places where the bricks have come away.

INSCRIPTIONS

Placed around four sides of the bridge, the inscription L . FABRICIVS . C . F . CVR . VIAR FACIVNDVM COERAVIT IDEMQVE PROBAVIT explains that Lucius Fabricius, the *curator viarum* who was responsible for Rome's road network, supervised the building of the structure and approved of the works. This declaration was made

in order to give the green light to the contractors who had to adhere to the rigorous principle that works were to be guaranteed for 40 years: only in the 41st year would the initial deposit, paid by them as caution money, be returned.

Another inscription on the bridge tells of improvements made in 21BC by consuls Marcus Lollius and Quintus Aemilius Lepidus – this may have been for restorations following a flood two years earlier. The works carried out in the 17th century under Pope Innocent XI are also marked by an inscription.

Name	Pons Fabricius
Location	Rome
Crosses	Tiber River
Type	Stone arch bridge
Function	Road bridge (now pedestrians only)
Spans	Two spans of 24.5m (80ft)
Length	62m (203ft)
Opened	62BC

Right Whilst the bridge itself is Roman, the marble pillars on the parapet, featuring the two-faced Janus, are more recent, having been moved here from the Church of St. Gregory in the 14th century.

THE BRIDGE OF SIGHS

VENICE / **ITALY**

A high walkway between the Palazzo Ducale, once home of the rulers of Venice, and the infamous St. Mark's prison, the Bridge of Sighs (Ponte dei Sospiri) has evoked romantic pity as well as artistic admiration, and has lent its name to imitations around the world.

DISTINCT STYLES

The design for an enclosed bridge was created by Antonio Contino, and built in white limestone between 1600 and 1603. It reconciles the distinct architectural styles of the late 16th-century prison with the palace of a century earlier with a bold span high above the canal, and has gained fame through associations created by 19th-century art and poetry.

Lord Byron was the first to bring the Bridge of Sighs to a wider public with his lengthy but immensely successful narrative poem *Childe Harold* (published 1812–18), drawing on the idea of innocent victims of the Inquisition snatching their last glimpse of Venice from the bridge before being led from torture to execution. J.M.W. Turner's painting of the bridge was famously exhibited in 1840 alongside Byron's words: 'I stood at Venice on the Bridge of Sighs/A palace and a prison on each hand'.

Although the bridge does indeed connect what were the interrogation rooms in the main palace with the prison, by the time it was built the worst excesses of the Inquisition were over, and the bridge was used simply to move common offenders from the prison to the judgement hall out of the public eye. In the cell blocks across the bridge, narrow corridors and steep stairways link the warren of cells, many of which have their number and capacity painted over the door.

BRIDGE OF INSPIRATION

In the 18th and 19th centuries, when wealthy young men were expected to visit Venice on the 'Grand Tour', the city's distinctive architecture became widely known among the educated classes. Therefore, it is not surprising that the bridge inspired similar constructions at Oxford and Cambridge colleges. Other bridges associated with pitiful stories acquired the name too, despite having no physical resemblance: London's old Waterloo Bridge was the setting for Thomas Hood's 1844 poem *The Bridge of Sighs*, describing the drowned body of a young woman who has committed suicide. Peru's version of the Bridge of Sighs is an open wooden walkway in Lima's resort area of Barranco, bordered by grand houses, from where a young women forbidden to see her low-born beloved is said to have waited patiently at her window.

Right Despite its past, the Bridge of Sighs has become a place of pilgrimage for lovers. Venetian legend says that if lovers kiss on a gondola under the bridge while the sun is setting, their love will be eternal.

Name	Bridge of Sighs
Location	Venice, Italy
Crosses	Rio di Palazzo
Type	Enclosed stone arch bridge
Function	Connecting buildings
Span	11m (36ft)
Opened	1603
Design	Antonio Contino

VENICE BRIDGE LOOK-ALIKES IN THE UNITED KINGDOM

In Cambridge, the so-called Bridge of Sighs at St. John's College was designed by Henry Hutchinson in 1827. In Pittsburgh, Pennsylvania, the Boston architect H.H. Richardson connected his 1886 Allegheny County Courthouse and prison with a granite Bridge of Sighs, the only look-alike with a similar function to the original. It blends the enclosed corridor feature of the Venice bridge with the more sloping profile of the Rialto Bridge. Oxford's Bridge of Sighs (1913) connects two parts of Hertford College and was designed by Sir Thomas Jackson.

Left The Oxford Bridge of Sighs was never intended to be a replica of its namesake and actually bears a closer resemblance to the Rialto Bridge in Venice.

RIALTO BRIDGE

VENICE / **ITALY**

In contrast to the grim mysteries of the Bridge of Sighs, the Rialto Bridge is a bustling and much-loved Venetian landmark. However, the two are linked; the Rialto's designer was also responsible for St. Mark's prison, and was the uncle of the architect of the Bridge of Sighs.

THE OLDEST CROSSING

Once Venice's commerical heart and probably the earliest part of the lagoon to be settled, a pontoon of boats had previously linked the two banks at Rialto in the 12th century. The oldest bridge across the Grand Canal, the Rialto replaced a wooden bridge of 1250 which had suffered from fire and collapse on several occasions. It was not until the 16th century that the Doge of Venice held a competition for a new design, which was won by Antonio da Ponte against some of the most celebrated architects of the age, including Andrea Palladio and Vincenzo Scamozzi. His single-span design very much followed the shape of the wooden bridge, with wide stepped ramps leading up to a central portico. Scamozzi meanwhile warned that the bridge would be a disaster, although some claim that this may have been because da Ponte had copied one of his designs. In fact the structure proved so strong that it withstood the force of a cannon being fired from its steps to dispel rioters in 1797.

BRIDGE OF COMMERCE

Construction began in 1588 and took only three years. The massive superstructure is still supported on some 12,000 wooden piles that were driven into the soft silty ground at that time. The Rialto Bridge remained the only way to cross the Grand Canal on foot until the Accademia Bridge was built in 1854. The walkway of the portico is lined with small shops now selling tourist goods, while two other walkways run along the balustrades. The fondamente (foundations) stretching below the bridge on either side of the water, are named for their original functions as unloading wharfs; the San Marco side is the Riva del Ferro, so called for the iron once unloaded here, while the Riva del Vin opposite recalls the thousands of wine barrels that once came ashore at this point.

TOURIST SITE

The bridge was an instant success with the Venetians, and has been described by Jan Morris in her book *The World of Venice* as 'one of the few Venetian monuments to possess the quality of geniality'. Some observers have pronounced it top-heavy and graceless, but as an icon of the city it is very much beloved and a popular place to head to for views at sunset.

Above and Right When it first opened, the Rialto, with its inclined ramps carrying rows of shops leading up to an ornate central portico, was thought to be so daring that some predicted its ruin.

Name	Rialto Bridge
Location	Venice, Italy
Crosses	Grand Canal
Type	Covered stone arch bridge
Function	Pedestrian bridge
Span	28.8m (94.5ft)
Length	48m (158ft)
Clearance	7.32m (24ft)
Constructed	1588–1591
Design	Antonio da Ponte

PONTE VECCHIO

FLORENCE / *ITALY*

Florence's most familiar sight, with its multi-coloured overhanging
shops and green shutters, the Ponte Vecchio has survived centuries
of wars and floods, and the omnipotent Medici family that had a great
influence on its fate.

PONTE VECCHIO

EARLY HISTORY

The Ponte Vecchio ('old bridge') crosses the narrowest point of the Arno River as it flows through the historic centre of Florence. Records of a span here go back to AD996, but it is thought that in Roman times there was a wooden bridge supported by stone piers, on the course of the Via Cassia (the Roman road that led out of the northwest of Rome) which crossed at this point. The five-arched predecessor of the current bridge was destroyed by a flood in 1333. Twelve years later, this broader three-arched structure was erected. Its shops were originally rented out by the city government, but later sold off and adapted by their owners. The back shops or *retrobotteghe* were added in the 17th century.

Above Shoppers peer through the madielles, the little display windows with shuttered windows of the jewellers' shops, which line the inside of the Florence's Ponte Vecchio.

BUTCHERS FOR BAUBLES

The first traders on the bridge were blacksmiths, butchers and tanners, serving the numerous travelling soldiers who passed this way. By 1442 a monopoly of butchers dominated the scene. Ferdinando I de' Medici, the Grand Duke of Tuscany and the then current ruling member of the Medici family, did not care for the unsavoury stench, and in 1593 evicted the butchers, replacing them with jewellers and goldsmiths. They have remained there ever since, with the more recent addition of art and souvenir shops. On the bridge is a bust of the foremost Renaissance Florentine goldsmith – also a painter and sculptor – Benvenuto Cellini (1500–71).

It is believed that the term 'bankrupt' originated here. Merchants sold their goods from tables in front of the premises; anyone unable to pay his debts had his table or *banco*, broken (*rotto*) by soldiers – the word *bancorotto* (bankrupt) was ascribed to them. In this state, without a table, they were no longer permitted to trade.

PRIVATE GALLERY

The Medicis certainly enjoyed a privileged view of the bridge. A special covered walkway, built by the painter and architect Vasari in 1565 under the orders of Cosimo I and known as the Vasari Corridor, runs above the shops on the bridge from the Uffizi art gallery to the Medicis' Palazzo Pitti. An unremarkable-looking door from the Uffizi leads into this secret place, which is open by appointment only, and thus seen by few visitors. It then runs above a colonnade and over the bridge high above the crowds of sightseers, past a specially constructed window that effectively forms a private gallery at the top of Santa Felicita Church, to end by the shell- and stalactite-encrusted Buontalenti Grotto. The Corridor now serves as repository for hundreds of self-portraits by various artists, while the larger windows were inserted by the Nazis to coincide with Hitler's wartime visit to Florence.

AVERTING DISASTER

The bridge had two narrow escapes during the 20th century. It was spared when the Nazis retreated from Florence on 4 August 1944. Hitler gave orders to blow up all the bridges except this unique medieval structure, which was instead rendered inaccessible by destroying the buildings on its approach routes. In November 1966 the bridge withstood a catastrophic flood following 40 days of rain (with half a metre (19.7 inches) falling in the preceding two days before the deluge). Many shops on it, along with much of the city, were devastated. Some goldsmiths might have lost all their stock had it not been for a night watchman who called the proprietors at their homes and alerted them to the rising waters.

Name	Ponte Vecchio
Location	Florence, Italy
Crosses	Arno River
Type	Arched stone bridge
Function	Road bridge
Main span	30m (98ft)
Length of side spans	27m (88ft)
Deck width	32m (105ft)

THE KRÄMERBRÜCKE ('MERCHANTS' BRIDGE'), ERFURT

Within one of the best-preserved medieval town centres in Germany, this stone six-arched bridge over Gera River is the only European bridge north of the Alps that is entirely built over with inhabited buildings. Anyone wandering along its cobbled street and unfamiliar with the city might not even notice that it is a bridge, as the tall buildings are continuous and on both sides. Like the Ponte Vecchio, it has a long history as a place of trading: for many years merchants carried out their trades from timber stands on the bridge and on its predecessors. The current structure dates from 1325 and was strengthened after a fire in 1472, when it was developed with shops with living quarters along its 120-metre (394-foot) length. The Ägidienkirche, originating as a bridge chapel for an earlier span and later rebuilt, is the lone survivor of a pair of medieval churches at each end of the bridge.

Right Thirty-two half-timbered dwellings line the length Krämerbrücke without a gap. Its name roughly translating as 'grocers' bridge', the structure has been used by tradespeople since the 12th century.

Right Aside from jewellers shops and boutiques, a number of people actually live in the buildings on the bridge with the apartments providing a good view of Florence and the River Arno.

VASCO DA GAMA BRIDGE

LISBON / **PORTUGAL**

Completed in time for Expo '98, which celebrated the 500th
anniversary of Portuguese explorer Vasco da Gama's discovery
of the sea route to India, this immense project was seen as
a symbol of Portugal's modernisation at the turn of the millennium.

DESIGN AND PURPOSE
The Tagus River is approximately 2km (1.2
miles) wide at Lisbon and before the opening
of the 25 de Abril suspension bridge in 1966
(see page 92) the nearest fixed crossing was
some 32km (20 miles) north of the city, via
a road bridge built in the 1930s. Since 1998,
the Vasco da Gama bridge has enabled traffic
to bypass the Portuguese capital altogether,
relieving pressure on the older bridge,
and providing a link between previously
unconnected motorways radiating from
Lisbon. The project was financed by a
Lusoponte, an international consortium
consisting of Portuguese, French and British

companies, with the help of EU cohesion
funds. In return, Lusoponte was awarded
the right to collect tolls from both Lisbon's
road bridges for 40 years.

BATTLING NATURAL FORCES
The bridge was designed to withstand wind
speeds of 250kph (155mph) and earthquakes
4.5 times stronger than the one which
devastated Lisbon in 1755, estimated at 8.7
on the Richter scale. Its foundation piles,
up to 2.2m (7.2ft) in diameter, reach to 95m
(312ft) below sea level. The bridge is so long
that the design also had to take into account
the curvature of the Earth – which would

Left During its three years of preparation and construction, up to 3,300
people worked simultaneously on the Vasco da Gama Bridge.

otherwise have produced an 80cm (2.6ft) deviation in height from one end to the other.

PROTECTING THE LOCAL AREA

In response to environmental concerns, the south viaduct was extended inland to preserve the marshland bird habitat of the Samouco Salt Pans beneath, and the lamps along the whole length of the bridge are tilted inwards to prevent light being cast on the river below. Some 300 families in the local area were rehoused to make way for the construction.

HEAVY-DUTY CONSTRUCTION

The construction of the bridge was divided into seven sections, separately managed; the access roads at each end, the north, south and central viaducts, the access viaduct to the Expo '98 site and the main bridge itself.

The main bridge consists of a central cable-stayed deck spanning 420m (1,378ft) and two side spans of 203m (666ft) each, giving 47m (154ft) of clearance for shipping in the north channel of the Tagus. The two great pylons in the shape of a splayed 'H' at each end are designed to survive the impact of a ship of up to 30,000 tonnes, travelling at 12 knots.

The central viaduct runs for more than 6km (3.7 miles), mostly at 14m (45.9ft) above the water. It rises to 30m (98.4ft) over two navigation channels to allow medium-sized ships to pass. It consists of 80 pre-fabricated sections 78m (256ft) long, which were manufactured nearby at a giant pre-casting yard at Seixal, 22km (13.7 miles) downstream. The yard produced one beam every two days, which was then transported to the bridge site on a giant crane vessel called the Rambiz.

Name	Vasco Da Gama Bridge
Location	Lisbon, Portugal
Crosses	Tagus River
Type	Cable-stayed
Function	Road Bridge (6 lanes)
Total length	17,185m (56,381ft)
Largest span	420m (1378ft)
Clearance	47m (154ft)
Pylon height	155m (509ft)
Design	Armando Rito

Right The deepest foundation piles (each 2.2m (7.2ft) in diameter) of the Vasco Da Gama Bridge were sunk up to 95m (312ft) under the average sea level.

LISBON'S OTHER GREAT BRIDGE: THE 25 DE ABRIL

Often compared to San Franciso's Golden Gate bridge, this Lisbon landmark does indeed have US parallels. It most closely resembles the San Francisco-Oakland Bay Bridge, and both were built to withstand the same kinds of earthquake threats that face both cities.

When it was completed in 1966, at a cost of $32 million US, it was the largest suspension bridge outside the USA, with the longest continuous truss and the deepest foundations – some 80 metres below the river bed – of any bridge in the world. Then known as the Salazar Bridge, after the Portuguese Prime Minister and dictator, it was renamed the 25 Abril Bridge to commemorate the 'Carnation Revolution' that toppled Salazar's successor in 1974.

The bridge is 2,277m (7,471ft) long with a main span of just over 1 km (0.6 miles). It originally opened as a four-lane road bridge with a central barrier, but the barrier was removed in 1990 to accommodate a fifth lane.

In 1998 the American Bridge Company was called back to 'retro-fit' railway tracks to the lower platform: materials were hauled up from ships below to avoid disrupting the traffic. The work included carrying out the first-ever aerial spinning operation to connect additional main cables to the bridge while it remained fully loaded and operational. In fact, from the outset the bridge was designed to have a lower railway deck, but this plan was aborted at the time of construction.

Despite the opening of this rail link and the Vasco da Gama Bridge, traffic levels have remained close to the bridge's capacity and the

Portuguese Government had announced an intention to seek tenders for a third road-rail crossing of the Tagus some 30km (18.6 miles) upstream from Lisbon.

Below In terms of design, the 25 de Abril bridge is most closely related to the San Francisco-Oakland Bay Bridge (see pages 236-237) and the Forth Road Bridge in Scotland. Upon completion, it was the fifth largest suspension bridge in the world.

ALAMILLO BRIDGE

SEVILLE / **SPAIN**

As the signature bridge for Expo '92, Seville's World Fair, the great inclined mast of this ground-breaking design seemed to point the way to the future. Spanish architect, sculptor and engineer Santiago Calatrava, among the most influential bridge designers of his time, has since won commissions for his distinctive bridges across the world.

A MEMORABLE STRUCTURE

The key innovation of the Alamillo Bridge was its striking asymmetry, due to its single angled, concrete-filled steel mast or pylon, the weight of which is enough to support the deck without the need for counter-stay cables on the other side. Whilst less efficient in structural terms than a symmetrical design, it makes for dramatic architecture. The 13 pairs of cables form a single plane supporting a beam down the middle of the roadway, suggesting the image of a harp. Originally the bridge was intended as one of a pair on either side of the island where the Expo was being held, with a connecting viaduct between the two; their sloping masts would have stretched towards each other and suggested a gigantic triangle in the air, visible from Seville's Old Town. According to Calatrava, the Seville authorities 'wanted to have something symbolic that could remain in the memory of visitors…like an "open arms" gesture'. However doubts about the design and costs meant the second bridge was never built.

Right Four new bridges were built to La Cartuja Island for Expo '92, but only the Alamillo Bridge has gone on to become a symbol of modern Seville.

94

Name	Alamillo Bridge
Location	Seville
Crosses	Guadalquivir River
Type	Cantilever spar cable-stayed
Function	Road and pedestrian bridge
Span	200m (656ft)
Length	250m (820ft)
Mast height	142m (466ft)
Opened	1992
Design	Santiago Calatrava

CALATRAVA

Born in 1951, Santiago Calatrava trained as an artist, civil engineer and architect, and fuses all three elements in his work. Winner of many design competitions and awards, his striking, usually bright white designs for bridges and other structures have become a central feature of high-profile urban development and regeneration projects around the turn of the millennium.

ANOTHER SPANISH COMMISSION

Another prestigious Spanish commission for Calatrava was the Campo Volantin footbridge, also known as the Zibizuri (Basque for 'white bridge'), with an inclined white-painted steel arch and a deck made largely of translucent structural glass. Opened in 1997, it provides a route for visitors walking from the hotel district to Bilbao's Guggenheim Museum. Although much admired, the bridge has also been criticised for impracticality; the glass tiles become slippery in rain and are expensive to replace, and it does not connect well to other destinations people want to walk to. In 2007, Calatrava unsuccessfully sued the authorities for breaching the integrity of his structure by cutting into part of it to attach a new walkway.

Right With the weight of the bridge supporting by its iconic single upward arm towering over the city of Seville, the Alamillo Bridge has been compared to a swan, a ship's mast, and a harp.

THE WORKS OF SANTIAGO CALATRAVA

Santiago Calatrava has been responsible for several much-lauded bridge projects across the world. His James Joyce bridge, opened in 2003, spans the River Liffey in Dublin and consists of two outward-leaning steel arches supporting the roadway as if by two handles. The first Calatrava bridge in the US was the 2004 Sundial Bridge, a footbridge in Redding, California. The tip of the shadow of the 217ft (66m) slanting mast, similar to that of the Alamillo Bridge, moves about a metre every three minutes and the time can be read at the other end on the world's largest sundial. The glass deck allows people on the bridge to look down at the boats passing underneath.

In the Netherlands, the district of Haarlemmermeer, near to Schiphol Airport, commissioned a family of three cable-stayed bridges with slanting masts along the Hoofdvaart canal, completed in 2004 as part of a new residential development and intended to reflect the district's progressive aspirations. Because their shape suggests musical instruments, they are known as the Harp, Zither and Lute bridges. Calatrava intended them to reflect the clean lines of the canal and the flat surrounding landscape.

In 1996 Calatrava offered to design a new pedestrian bridge for the Grand Canal in Venice, only its fourth crossing, to link the centre to the railway station and main bus terminal and car park area, the Piazzale Roma. In a departure from his signature white cable-stayed designs, the glass and steel arch span, completed in 2007, blends unobtrusively with its surroundings.

Among the more controversial Calatrava designs is the Chords Bridge or Bridge of Strings in Jerusalem, carrying a light rail system and inaugurated in June 2008 as part of the state of Israel's celebrations of the 60th anniversary of its founding. At 118 metres, its angular leaning mast is the tallest structure in Jerusalem. Some have argued that it is inappropriate in a crowded and dilapidated setting; others see it as a powerful symbol of urban renewal and a welcome new secular symbol for a divided city.

Below Calatrava's Sundial Bridge in Redding, California, provides a pedestrian walkway between the north and south areas of the Turtle Bay Exploration Park. The translucent glass of the decking glows aquamarine at night.

ALCANTARA BRIDGE

ALCANTARA / **SPAIN**

This astonishing survival is acknowledged widely as an outstanding example of Roman bridge building. Its square granite piers bear the roadway 57m (187ft) over the Tagus River, higher than the clearance of the Forth Bridge or that of the Sydney Harbour Bridge.

ROMAN INSCRIPTION

Remarkably for a bridge of such antiquity, we actually know the architect's name. Caius Iulius Lacer's name was recorded for posterity in an inscription on a lintel placed on the commemorative temple by the entrance. Such public works of architecture as this would have been funded by local resources or private enterprise; here, the inscription bears the names of the towns that contributed to the cost of building. No record exists, however, of the method of construction. It is likely slave and prison labour would have been used, but the process of how the arches were erected and the centering completed remains a mystery. Frequent floods would have hampered progress, and scaffolding could have easily been washed away.

HISTORY IN THE MAKING

Alcantara takes its name from the Arabic *al qantarat* for bridge; the same name is given to a later bridge at Toledo. This structure in the Extremadura region was erected on the Roman road that connected Norba – today (known as Cáceres) with Conimbriga (now called Condeixa-a-Velha, and over the border in Portugal).

The bridge is held together without mortar, reinforced in part by iron staples, and with some stones placed at right angles to the rest to give more solidity. The arch spans

Name	Alcantara Bridge
Location	Alcantara, Spain
Crosses	Río Tajo
Type	Granite arched bridge
Function	Road bridge
Main span	28.8m (94.5ft)
Length	194m (637ft)
Clearance	57m (187ft)
Design	Caius Iulius Lacer
Opened	AD106

range from 13.8m (44ft) at each bank to 28.8m (94.5ft) across the river. The bridge has not come through 2,000 years unscathed. It was partially destroyed by the Moors in 1214, then in 1812 French soldiers demolished one of the arches when facing the hostility of the Duke of Wellington's army. As a result, it has been restored on several occasions.

INSCRIPTIONS

The 8-metre (26-foot) wide roadway passes beneath a rectangular 13-metre (43-foot) tall triumphal arch at the centre of the bridge. Inscriptions on marble plates here provide the date of building, and explain the arch was built in honour of the Roman Emperor Trajan. In 1543 another plaque was added for Emperor Charles V, with a double-headed eagle, the arms of the Habsburgs and Bourbons.

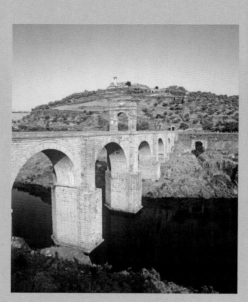

Above and Right An impressive remnant of Roman Hispania, the Alcantara Bridge is supported by three great arches on the water and three smaller arcs set into the earth on either side of the river.

PUENTE NUEVO

RONDA / **SPAIN**

The two halves of the town of Ronda in southern Spain are joined by the Puente Nuevo (new bridge), completed in 1793. Appearing to grow from the surrounding cliffs, it fills the Tajo gorge with immense columns of golden limestone, pierced by four round-headed arches.

Name	Puente Nuevo
Location	Ronda, Spain
Crosses	Tajo Gorge
Length	33.5m (110ft)
Total height	98m (322ft)
Pier height	92m (302ft)
Completed	1793
Design	José Martin de Aldehuela

Left and Above The 18th-century arched bridge spans the El Tajo gorge and connects the modern market quarter with the old quarter of the town. The whole structure took 42 years to build.

EARLIER SPANS

The choice of such a sturdy structure is no matter of chance. A previous attempt to span the gorge with a single stone arch had ended in tragedy after only six years when it collapsed in 1741 with the loss of 50 lives. Some attributed the failure to a faulty design chosen by King Philip V of Spain, who had commissioned the works; others blamed the bridge builders, Juan Camacho and José Garcia, who built it in only eight months.

A new crossing was certainly needed. The only other bridge, that eventually became known as the Puente Viejo (old bridge), dated from the 16th century and set far below in the gorge. It was regularly flooded by the Guadalquivín River in spate, and required an arduous descent and climb to connect the old town and the newer commercial centre around the market. The architect, José Martin de Aldehuela (1729–1802), was based in the regional capital of Malaga where he had originally been engaged by the Bishop to complete the cathedral. He was diverted from this to work on the San Telmo aqueduct, which finally brought fresh water to the city, and never paid for his cathedral works.

A LENGTHY CONSTRUCTION

It took more than 40 years to construct de Aldehuela's bridge design. The chief builder, Juan Antonio Díaz Machuca, a native of Ronda, invented a series of machines to help raise the huge stone blocks taken from the bottom of the gorge. Curious legends then arose about de Aldehuela. One said that he had thrown himself from the parapet because he knew he could never again design anything so beautiful. More prosaically, another claimed that he simply slipped and fell while carrying out a final inspection. In reality, he died of natural causes in Malaga nearly ten years after the bridge was finished. He was deeply in debt and had not been fully paid for Puente Nuevo or for his following work on the Ronda bullring.

TRAGEDY AND VIOLENCE

The height of the bridge and the shallow parapet creates a sense of vertigo in many visitors, heightened by the knowledge that many accidents, suicides and acts of violence have taken place here over the centuries. Above the main arch is a small chamber now housing an interpretation centre but once used as a prison. Both sides in the Spanish Civil War are said to have tortured prisoners there. Ernest Hemingway drew on events in Ronda in *For Whom the Bell Tolls*, where he describes hundreds of alleged Fascist sympathisers being flung into the gorge, but this was from the cliffs rather than the bridge itself.

101

NEW ARSTA BRIDGE

STOCKHOLM / SWEDEN

Stockholm is built on an archipelago of 14 islands and as such is dependent on its numerous bridges. It reaffirmed its commitment to public transport with the New Arsta Bridge, more than doubling the capacity of its Central Station.

THE ORIGINAL BRIDGE

Some 500 trains a day cross the Årstaviken channel between one of the major islands, Södermalm and Stockholm's southern mainland district Årsta, crossing a small island mid-way. Until the opening of the new bridge in 2005, the trains all used the original Arsta Bridge, which dates to 1929. Compared by some to a Roman aqueduct, this was the longest bridge in Sweden when it opened, stretching 753m (2,471ft) and including a truss arch span and a lift bridge. It was designed by Swedish architect Cyrillus Johansson, and is now listed as a

historic landmark. Before the bridge was even finished, the city authorities were discussing adding an iron road deck above the railway lines. They required the design to be strengthened with this in mind, and specified a lifting section instead of the planned bascule over the northern channel.

The idea of a road deck was revived several times during the 20th century, and in 1960 a motorway bridge running parallel on the west side was proposed as an extension to the city ring road. However, towards the end of the century, it became clear that

Left The distinctive red of Foster's New Arsta Bridge, also known as the Western Arsta Bridge, sits alongside its neighbour, the Old Arsta Bridge; collectively, they are called the Årstabroarna.

103

modernising the railway network was more pressing. Two more tracks were needed to avoid rush-hour gridlocks on the commuter rail system, but as a listed structure the original bridge could not now be altered.

A NEW ARSTA

Foster and Partners, together with Ove Arup, won an international competition in 1994 to design a second bridge. Their New Arsta Bridge was intended to complement the original bridge and the landscape and cityscape it served. It brought the public benefits of a walkway and cycleway alongside the railway tracks, as well as a new commuter railway station on its south side. It also helped the regeneration of the run-down areas along the waterfronts, including new housing and commercial schemes. The railway tracks are inset in a trough in the deck, with special sound absorbent finishes and cushioning to help cut down environmental noise.

Sited just 45m (148ft) west of the old bridge, the rounded contours and elliptical piers of the new bridge respond to the surrounding landscape. The designers term this 'calming geometry', intended as a response to the tranquillity of the Årstaviken Bay and to make the bridge recede into its setting. Its deep red colour echoes the traditional finish (known as falu red) used on Stockholm's old wooden buildings. In a further reference to traditional methods, the concrete under-surface was poured into formwork made of solid timber planks, creating a subtle wood-textured finish. At the inauguration of the bridge on 30 August 2005, Lord Foster said, "We have tried to respond sensitively to the surrounding landscape by creating a bridge that merges seamlessly with its context.'

CONCRETE AND COLOUR

Although the idea of a red-coloured concrete bridge aroused some scepticism during the planning process, the new bridge is now viewed as a visual success, with the pigmented material overcoming the disadvantage of unfinished concrete appearing discoloured in the relatively wet Swedish concrete. Some 23,000 cubic metres of coloured concrete were used in the new structure. This was selected over a painted finish for better ease of maintenance, durability and engineering qualities. The process of adding the special iron-ore pigment powder to the concrete requires precision to ensure consistent colour and an even mix: the project represented a major challenge for the suppliers, Lanxess, and has been the subject of technical case studies. As well as fulfilling the colour specifications, they needed to guarantee that the concrete could be transported for long distances and would arrive at exactly the right consistency to be pumped and poured, without leaving gaps and without weakening or cracking when it dried. The concrete-pouring took place from a 130-metre (427-foot) platform which was fixed to the sections that had already been completed and supported by the next two piers, then moved along to complete the next sections. To ensure an even colour tone to the surface, the wooden formwork was coated with red-pigmented cement. And as befits a bridge with 'green' credentials, environmental protection was one of the construction principles, with the impact of dyes, chemicals and emissions minimised.

Name	New Arsta Bridge
Location	Stockholm, Sweden
Crosses	Årstaviken Bay
Type	Concrete viaduct bridge
Function	Rail, pedestrian and cycle
Spans	10 columns supporting 65 to 78-metre spans
Length	833m (2,733ft)
Clearance	26m (85.3ft)
Opened	2005
Design	Foster and Partners

Right The deep red colour used on the New Arsta is known as falu red. A traditional shade, it has been used on wooden cottages and barns in Sweden since the 17th century.

KAPELLBRÜCKE

LUCERNE / **SWITZERLAND**

The much-cherished 700-year-old Kapellbrücke (Chapel Bridge) is the longest and oldest covered wooden bridge in Europe, painstakingly reconstructed after a disastrous fire in 1993. The Spreuer Bridge, also in Lucerne, has many similarities with this remarkable structure.

A VERSATILE STRUCTURE

Crossing obliquely over the Reuss River at the mouth of Lake Lucerne (also known as the Lake of the Four Forest Cantons), this originates as a part of Lucerne's fortifications. The chapel after which it is named is St Peterskapelle (St. Peter's Chapel), which stands nearby at the entrance of the bridge on the left bank of the river.

In the early 17th century the gabled roof was adorned with more than 100 triangular painted panels depicting the history and mythology of Lucerne and the surrounding area, and the town's patron saints St. Leodegar and St. Maurice. At the middle of the bridge is the octagonal 34.5-metre (113.2-foot) tall Wasserturm, which has served variously as a dungeon, a torture chamber, a lighthouse, an archive and a treasury vault.

FIRE AND RECONSTRUCTION

Shortly after midnight on 18 August 1993, fire probably caused by a smouldering cigarette left on a boat moored beneath destroyed about two-thirds of the bridge, sparing the pillars, the bridgeheads and the Water Tower. Reconstruction was rapid and dramatic; within eight months it was complete, and very much back to what it was before. Only a third of the 122 paintings escaped damage; those destroyed have been replicated or replaced by others that had been in storage. The $2.1 million reconstruction programme was funded by insurance, donations and revenue from a specially issued postage stamp.

THE SPREUER: A CLOSE RELATION

Downstream, Lucerne retains another remarkable wooden covered bridge, the Spreuer Bridge. As well as a small chapel, it features in its gables a remarkable set of 67 early 17th-century paintings by Kaspar Meglinger on the theme of the Dance of Death – reflecting attitudes to death at a time when the plague was rife. Dating from around 1408 and rebuilt in 1568, it originally served to connect the mills with the bakers'

quarter in Pfistergasse on the left bank of the River Reuss. This was located on the opposite bank from the medieval town and was a deliberate plan to avoid fire spreading from bakers' stoves. As the bridge was downstream of the town, millers were permitted to throw their waste wheat chaff – Spreu (after which the bridge takes its name) – into the river there.

Name	Kapellbrücke
Location	Lucerne
Crosses	Reuss River (at the mouth of Lake Lucerne)
Type	Wooden covered bridge
Function	Pedestrian bridge
Length	285m (935ft)
Opened	1333; rebuilt 1994

Right The Wassterturm, or Water Tower, has survived from the Kapellbrucke's construction, and still forms part of the Lucerne city walls. The bridge is the most photographed landmark in Switzerland.

STONE BRIDGE
OF ADANA

ADANA / TURKEY

Bridge building in the Roman Empire, as can be seen with the Pont du
Gard aqueduct, was for a long time without par and unprecedented in
scale. Roman engineers introduced pioneering techniques such as the
use of natural cement and the development of the semicircular arch.

Left The Severan Bridge, also named the Chabinas Bridge or Cendere Bridge, is one of the largest arches known to be built by the Romans. It is still in use and vehicles up to 5 tonnes are allowed to cross the arch.

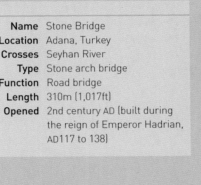

THE BRIDGE AT ADANA

Once a vital crossing on the historic trade routes from Persia into the European continent, the great Stone Bridge of Adana dates from the 2nd century AD and today is the only Roman bridge in existence still open to vehicle traffic.

Adana, colonised by the Romans in 66BC, is at the heart of southern Turkey's fertile agricultural plain, and with a population of over a million, is now the country's fourth largest city. Little remains of the ancient city's built environment except the bridge,

which owes its good condition to a history of careful repairs over the centuries, (under Emperor Justinian in the 6th century AD and under Muslim rulers in AD742 and 840). Of the original 21 arches, 14 are still standing, arranged in a distinctive asymmetric pattern.

THE SEVERAN BRIDGE

Another remarkable Roman-era bridge in southern Turkey is the Severan Bridge near the ancient city of Arsameia (now Eskikale). Unlike the multi-arched Adana bridge, it has a single span of 34.2m (112ft) – the

second longest stone span of any surviving Roman bridge. Named after the Libyan-born Roman Emperor Septimius Severus (reign AD193-211), a Latin inscription on the bridge records that it was built to honour the Emperor, his second wife and their two sons, Caracalla and Geta. Each was represented by one of four Corinthian columns flanking the bridge. However, in a brutal reminder of Imperial Roman politics, Geta's column was later taken down after his brother succeeded to the throne, had Geta and his family assassinated and ordered all reminders of him to be removed throughout the Empire.

Name	Stone Bridge
Location	Adana, Turkey
Crosses	Seyhan River
Type	Stone arch bridge
Function	Road bridge
Length	310m (1,017ft)
Opened	2nd century AD (built during the reign of Emperor Hadrian, AD117 to 138)

Right Stretching across the Seyhan River, the lifeblood of the productive agricultural land of the area, the Stone Bridge in Adana is one of the oldest bridges in the world still in use.

ARKADIKO BRIDGE, GREECE

The ancient Greeks influenced the Roman Empire in many ways, but Roman bridge technology owes more to the Etruscan civilization of northern Italy than it did to the Greeks. The stone arch constructed with stones shaped into wedges or *voussoirs* was known to the Etruscans, whereas ancient Greek bridges used the more basic corbelling technique, of bringing successive layers of stones closer together until they met. Corbel bridges tend to be limited to small spans, and not very durable, but remarkably, some Greek bridges of this type survive from as early as the Late Bronze Age, dating from around 1300BC to 1190BC.

Arkadiko, or the Kazarma Bridge, is the best-known of four corbel arch bridges on the Peloponnese Peninsula, west of Athens. Twenty-two metres (72ft) long, it still bridges a 4-metre (13-foot) deep gully on what was the Nauplion-Epidaurus highway. This formed part of a military road network created by the Mycenaean Empire, Europe's first major civilization, which spread from its nearby base of Mycenae.

Small culverts under the roads were bridged using a simple post-and-lintel system, with stones laid flat, but larger streams and culverts had bridges made using a corbelling technique, bringing successive layers of limestone boulders on each side of a gap closer together until they form a simple arch.

This style of construction, consisting of natural unworked stones fitted together without mortar, is known as Cyclopean, a term derived from the Cyclopes, the blacksmiths to the gods, fierce creatures with one eye in the middle of their foreheads who were supposed to have built the massive fortifications at Tiryns and Mycenae. The Mycenean civilization gave rise to the writings of Homer and Hesiod, source of many surviving myths and legends that give a glimpse of the beliefs of the Bronze Age, when building in stone and forging metal would have been a mysterious secret to most people, and must at one time have seemed the work of supernatural beings.

THE POSTBRIDGE CLAPPER BRIDGE

POSTBRIDGE, DEVON / **UNITED KINGDOM**

Situated at the heart of the Dartmoor National Park, the clapper bridge at Postbridge is one of the finest surviving bridges of its kind. Found mostly on the moors of Devon, but also in other areas such as Snowdonia, Lancashire and the Isle of Anglesey, clapper bridges are created from large flat slabs of granite or schist supported on strong stone piers.

BRIDGING THE STEPPING STONES

The name of this type of bridge is said to be derived from the Anglo-Saxon *cleaca* which means 'bridging the stepping stones'. Difficult to date, such spans were once all assumed to be prehistoric. With their stone uprights crowned with slab tops, these structures date from the late Neolithic period, some 4,000 to 5,000 years ago, and many examples can still be seen across upland Devon and Cornwall. It is not hard to imagine that the people who constructed them could have built bridges using similar techniques. Once they had mastered manoeuvring heavy stones about,

using them for bridge-building would seem an obvious next step after employing tree trunks and planks for the purpose. Once in place, a stone bridge would be less likely to become slippery, rot or be dislodged by floodwater.

MEDIEVAL STRUCTURES

Dartmoor's surviving clapper bridges are all from the medieval period. At Postbridge, the construction is thought to date from the early 14th century, by which time many of the nearby moorland farms had become established. The place-name comes from the Dartmoor term for the slabs: 'posts'. By

Right The Postbridge Clapper bridge was built originally to help pack horses and workers heading to the Tavistock tin mines cross the East Dart River.

THE POSTBRIDGE CLAPPER BRIDGE

the 16th century Dartmoor had become the richest source of tin in Europe, thanks partly to these bridges which enabled packhorses to transport supplies in all weathers. However, the earliest known documented reference is not found until the mid-1600s.

During the 18th century, such modest historic features in the landscape were becoming appreciated by romantically minded travellers. In 1795, the Reverend John Swete wrote in his *Illustrated Journals of Georgian Travels in Devon* 'tis impossible to form an impression of a Structure, more simple than this, or better adapted to the situation...'.

Name	Postbridge Clapper Bridge
Location	Postbridge, Devon
Crosses	East Dart River
Type	Stone clapper bridge
Function	Pedestrian bridge
Span	Three 4-metre (13ft) spans
Length	12.95m (42.5ft)
Clearance	2 metres (6.6ft)
Built	1300s

CONSTRUCTION

The bridge itself is 12.95m (42.5ft) long and consists of four slabs of granite, one from each bank and two smaller slabs in the middle. The side slabs weigh an estimated 6.5 to 8 tonnes each and the two central sections around 2 tonnes apiece. The main supporting piers are built from five to six courses of stone, with a pointed 'cutwater' on the one exposed to the strongest flow. The cutwater, a structural device that helps the pier better resist the action of the water, is an early example of a design feature that this clapper bridge has in common with much more massive and sophisticated river crossings. The bridge would have required considerable effort to build; sleds and ponies would have been used to drag the stone from local sources. Tests show that the granite slabs have different feldspar content and so it is likely that they were taken from two separate local locations.

NATURAL MATERIALS

In a region where stone splits naturally into flat planes, laying slabs across a set of supports to form a clapper bridge is the easiest solution to bridging a wide span.

For narrower crossings, a simple form of cantilevering could have been used by bringing the higher layers of stone further together until they could be bridged at the top by a single slab. A good example is the Brontë Bridge at Haworth, Yorkshire, which was reconstructed in 1990. Here, the natural stone forms rounded or irregular shapes rather than flat slabs, bringing the courses of stones together on each bank closer together until they met would give a simple corbel arch of the kind seen in the 3,000-year-old bridge at Arkadiko (see page 111).

Since the 19th century, the clapper bridge at Postbridge has undergone various repair and restoration work, not least after a local farmer tipped one of the central slabs into the water in a failed attempt to dam the river (the stone fell flat on the river bed). It was superseded in the 1780s by a newer structure built upstream but remains a firm local favourite with historians and tourists.

Right The 14th-century bridge has withstood the test of time. However, it was superseded by another bridge across the East Dart in the late 18th century (see background).

ANPING BRIDGE, CHINA

In a remarkable development of the clapper bridge technique, the 12th-century Anping Bridge crosses 2,223m (7293ft) across a bay in Fujian Province, China, and was the longest bridge in the country until as late as 1905. Its 3- to 4-metre (9.8- to 13-foot) wide deck is made of stone beams side by side, with the largest beam weighing 25 tonnes. The bridge was originally embellished with stone statues of lions and generals and with pavilions, one of which survives along with 13 surrounding stone tablets recording the story of the bridge's building and repairs.

Left With construction lasting for 13 years during the Southern Song Dynasty, the Anping Bridge is the largest clapper bridge in the world. The 331 bridge piers that survive have three forms: cubic, boat-shaped, and semi-boat-shaped.

MATHEMATICAL BRIDGE

CAMBRIDGE / **UNITED KINGDOM**

On every Cambridge tourist's itinerary, and the subject of a series of remarkably durable myths, the so-called Mathematical Bridge spans the River Cam and joins two parts of Queens' College, Cambridge University. Built in 1749 and reconstructed in 1866 and 1905, its timber design is a rare example of the work of William Etheridge (1709–1776).

A NOTIONAL CURVE

The key feature of the Mathematical Bridge is its system of tangent-and-radial trussing, where the apparently curved arch is actually constructed of a series of straight timbers set at overlapping tangents to the notional curve of the bridge. This means that each piece of wood is held in compression with minimal bending movement, a system well suited to the material. The joints where the timbers cross are not load-bearing, but simply bolted to prevent lateral movement. Rigidity is provided by the radial timbers linking the arch to the top rail which create strong triangles and lock the whole structure together.

The term Mathematical Bridge may be derived from the 18th-century description of such designs as 'geometrical constructions'. Contrary to one of the associated myths, it has no connection with Cambridge mathematician and physicist Sir Isaac Newton, who died in 1727, more than 20 years before the bridge was built.

BRIDGE MYTHS

Another well-worn myth is that the bridge was originally constructed without any nails or bolts. The story goes that curious students or college Fellows took it apart to see how it was constructed – which would have been a very surprising feat considering

Left The Mathematical Bridge is a favourite on the Cambridge tourist trail. The current structure, built in 1905, replicated earlier designs. William Etheridge, who first built the bridge, was paid £21 for his inital design and model.

the weight and size of the timbers – and then could not put it back together again properly. The origins of this belief may lie in the fact that in its original and 1866 versions, the joints of the bridge were held by iron pins or screws, which were not readily apparent to the casual observer. Whereas the latest reconstruction of 1905 the pins were replaced by nuts and bolts (the bolt heads became visible to people passing over the bridge). Queens' College has a model of the bridge, thought to be Etheridge's original of 1748, and even this has screws at the joints.

WILLIAM ETHERIDGE

Further Mathematical Bridge myths are that William Etheridge had been a College student, and that he had been inspired by bridges seen on a visit to China. He was in fact descended from a long-established family of master carpenters from Suffolk, and is recorded as working on the first Westminster Bridge between 1738 and 1749. He also designed the three-arched wooden bridge at Walton on Thames (built 1748-1750), which was much admired and twice painted by Canaletto, but sadly decayed and survived only until 1783. After working on the Queens' bridge design and model, for which he was paid £21, Etheridge

went on to become the surveyor for the construction of the harbour at Ramsgate.

CONSTRUCTION AND REPLACEMENT

The Mathematical Bridge was built by James Essex the Younger (1722–1784), whose father James had also worked in many Cambridge colleges. Queens' College records show that 'Mr Essex's bill for the new bridge' was £160, and that a further 17 shillings and ninepence was paid to the Cook on 'a Supper on finishing the Bridge to Mr Essex's men'. Essex went on to construct the college's Essex Building, and in 1769 he built another bridge of similar design in Cambridge, between Trinity Hall and Trinity College on the site of the present Garret Hostel Bridge.

After a century or more, the Mathematical Bridge was badly decayed with its sides apparently leaning inwards. The repairs of 1866 replaced the original steps with sloping decking, enabling trolleys to be pushed over the bridge, but this may not have been a complete rebuilding: if some original decayed timbers were retained, this could explain why the repairs lasted less than four decades. In 1905 it was reconstructed completely, in teak rather than oak, by local builder William Sindall, and this is the version seen today.

Right and below The Mathematical Bridge is built entirely from straight timbers set at angles to present a notional curve. It connects the newer and older halves of Queens' College.

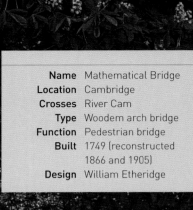

Name	Mathematical Bridge
Location	Cambridge
Crosses	River Cam
Type	Woodem arch bridge
Function	Pedestrian bridge
Built	1749 (reconstructed 1866 and 1905)
Design	William Etheridge

CONSTRUCTING THE FIRST WESTMINSTER BRIDGE

The earliest recorded example of the system of tangent-and-radial trussing (as used in the Mathematical Bridge) was James King's 1737 design for a wooden bridge at Westminster. However, this was abandoned in favour of a stone-built design after the piles were damaged when the Thames froze over in the winter of 1739-40. King's services were retained to construct wooden arches over which the stone arches could be put together, while still allowing shipping to pass. William Etheridge, King's master carpenter, took over the work after King's death in 1744, and used this system of trussing again in his own designs. While working at Westminster he is credited with inventing a special saw to cut off piles underwater.

Several paintings by Canaletto show the construction of the Westminster Bridge in progress. One erroneously depicts the wooden arch as consisting of curved timbers, rather than the intersecting straight sections set at a tangent which were the essential feature of the design, which suggests the artist could not have observed the structure very closely. The first bridge was eventually damaged by increased tidal flow and was replaced by the present cast-iron bridge in 1862.

Right Canaletto's depiction of Westminster Bridge from the north. Only the second bridge across the Thames below Kingston when it opened, the first Westminster Bridge was paid for by Parliament.

THE IRON BRIDGE

IRONBRIDGE, SHROPSHIRE / **UNITED KINGDOM**

Perhaps the most potent symbol of the early Industrial Revolution, this bridge is not only the first iron bridge but the first use of mass-produced cast-iron components in a structure of any kind.

A FAMILY REVOLUTION

Erected in the gorge of the River Severn by the ironmaster Abraham Darby III in 1779, the Iron Bridge was opened on 1 January 1781. The simplicity of its name hints at the immense significance of the structure, sited at the hub of an area that became busy with all kinds of manufacturing, not least iron, but also china, tiles and clay tobacco pipes.

The story begins with Darby's grandfather, Abraham Darby I, who leased a foundry in nearby Coalbrookdale. In 1709, he was the first to find a method of smelting iron using cheap, readily available coke, manufactured by processing coal, instead of the more expensive charcoal, (the production of which

was decimating local forests). Coal had proved unsuitable for the smelting task, because the sulphur content caused the iron to be brittle when hot; however, Darby found that the process of smelting using coke did not result in this problem. His method paved the way for mass-production of iron, and Britain's new industrial age dawned along with it. This new wonder material was turned to all sorts of uses, including cooking-pots, boilers, fireplaces and utensils.

THE NECESSITY FOR A CROSSING

Within decades, the Severn gorge became a hive of industrial activity, with a denser concentration of iron foundries along 3km

Left A few years after the bridge was completed, ground movement caused cracks to appear in the masonry abutments. By 1802, the southern abutment had to be demolished and eventually replaced by iron arches.

(1.9 miles) of the valley than anywhere else in the world. As the population of the area increased so did the need for crossings over the river for the workforce and the movement of raw materials.

CAST-IRON PROPOSAL

The idea for using iron to create a new crossing was first aired by the Shrewsbury architect Thomas Farnolls Pritchard who in 1773 wrote to the ironmaster John 'Iron Mad' Wilkinson proposing a bridge to be made of cast iron. Pritchard drew up a design and shares were issued to raise £3,200. His design was modified, with a wider roadway and a taller but narrower arch. An Act of Parliament was passed in 1776 'for building a Bridge across the River Severn from Benthall to the opposite shore at Madeley Wood' to avoid the 'great inconveniences, delays and obstructions, by reason of the insufficiency of the present ferry'; this prohibited ferries from operating within 500 yards of the bridge. There seems to have been a change of heart, as when tenders were invited, an instruction was issued to build using conventional

materials of stone, brick or timber. However, whatever nervousness existed about iron was somehow overcome and Abraham Darby III was commissioned to build the structure. There is virtually no record about how the structure was manufactured and installed – although a contemporary watercolour sketch came to light in 1997, showing the work in progress, with three of the five iron frames in place along with temporary supports – but it must have been a formidable undertaking, especially taking into account the need to hoist and position each 6-tonne iron half rib. While the method of making iron by smelting coke was by now no longer a novelty, nothing had ever been cast on this scale before. It seems likely that when Darby's furnace was enlarged in 1777, it was specifically for this purpose.

MADE TO FIT

The majority of the components were specially made to fit, and adapted the traditional mortice and dovetail joints used in woodwork; nut and bolt fixings were also used, creating an unprecedented and overcomplicated hybrid of joinery and

engineering techniques. The cast iron itself was not then fully understood as a material: 384 tonnes of it went into the structure – much more than was actually necessary. Each of the five ribs was cast in two pieces. Erection took three months. Its appearance astonished many; 'a striking effect in landscape and a stupendous specimen of the powers of mechanism' wrote one observer in 1798.

TOLL NOTICE

A year and a half after its completion, the bridge opened with various tolls charged for crossing it – a halfpenny for pedestrians, a penny for cattle, threepence for a laden horse or mule, and two shillings for a carriage drawn by six horses. Darby affixed a note beneath the table of tolls in accordance with his pacifist Quaker principles that 'This Bridge being private property, every Officer or Soldier, whether on duty or not, is liable to pay toll for passing over'. Tolls continued to be charged until 1950, although the bridge has been closed to road traffic since 1934. It is now in the care of English Heritage.

Name	The Iron Bridge
Location	Ironbridge, Shropshire
Crosses	River Severn
Type	Cast-iron arch bridge
Function	Road bridge
Span	30.5m (100ft)
Length	60m (197ft)
Clearance	18m (59ft)
Opened	1781 (completed 1779)
Design	Abraham Darby III

Left The largest single elements of the bridge are the half-ribs, each about 21.3 metres (70ft) long. In total the bridge is made up of more than 800 castings of 12 different basic types.

Right The area around Ironbridge is known as the birthplace of the Industrial Revolution, but the town itself grew up largely as a result of interest in the bridge, which had become an 18th century tourist attraction.

THE AFTERMATH OF THE IRON BRIDGE

Among other local iron-themed 18th-century innovations in Shropshire are the first iron-framed building (near Shrewsbury, 1796), Thomas Telford's aqueduct at Longdon on Tern (1796) and a cast-iron bridge at Cound Arbour (1797). The unlikely successor to Abraham Darby III was the republican Thomas Paine (1737–1809), the author of the radical pamphlets *Common Sense* and *The Rights of Man* and who played active roles in the French and American Revolutions. He turned his fertile mind for a period to the problems of iced-up rivers, and proposed the construction of bridges with long iron spans. To show how this could be achieved, in 1790 he erected a complete iron bridge on Paddington Green in London. However, the work of others soon eclipsed his scheme, and the project was abandoned.

CLIFTON SUSPENSION BRIDGE

CLIFTON, NEAR BRISTOL / **UNITED KINGDOM**

Ninety years in total from its inception to its eventual opening, the first major work of Isambard Kingdom Brunel was not completed until after the engineer's death. It has since become an international symbol of the city of Bristol.

BRUNEL'S FIRST CHALLENGE

The idea of building a bridge over the Clifton Gorge can be traced back to 1754, when a wealthy Bristol wine merchant, William Vick, left a legacy of £1,000 to build a stone bridge over the gorge, with instructions that the project should begin when the interest had accumulated tenfold. Indeed, on the Leigh Woods pier of the current bridge the Latin inscription 'Suspensa Vix Via Fit' roughly translates as 'a suspended way (or road) made with difficulty' – 'vix' being a pun on the name of William Vick.

By 1829 it was clear that the money (then £8,000) was not nearly enough to build such a stone construction, and an Act of Parliament was passed to allow for the erection of a wrought-iron suspension toll bridge instead. Accordingly a competition was held, with the great engineer of the day Thomas Telford as the judge. Telford actually selected his own design as the winner. It had a shorter main span than what we see today, with much taller, ornate Gothic piers that would have been positioned on the floor of the gorge rather than up the side of it. But the idea of Telford selecting his own project was unpopular, and another competition was held the following year. Brunel, then 24, was appointed project engineer. It was to be his first major commission, and one he was never to see completed.

Left While they are similar in size, the towers that anchor the bridge are not completely identical. The Clifton tower has cut outs in the sides, while the Leigh tower's arches are more pointed.

Left Affording spectacular views of the Avon Gorge, the Clifton Suspension Bridge is now a Grade I listed building. It was the centrepiece of the celebrations to mark the 200th anniversary of Brunel's birth in 2006.

LONG OR SHORT SPAN?

In all, Brunel proposed four different designs for a bridge over the Clifton Gorge. All of these were longer than the Menai Bridge of 1826, and two of them would even have exceeded the span of Joseph Chaley's Grand Pont Suspendu in Fribourg, Switzerland, then the world's longest bridge, with a main span of 273m (896ft). Telford had seen his own Menai Suspension Bridge damaged by crosswinds and was sceptical about the feasibility of building another suspension bridge in such an exposed position. The design that was finally selected had a shorter span.

Work started in 1831, but progress soon ground to a halt because of the Bristol Riots of 1831, as a result of which there was a loss of commercial confidence in grand building schemes in the city. After building resumed five years later and the foundation stone was laid, it transpired that the funds were inadequate. By 1843 only the towers had been built, but they were not yet finished when the money ran out completely. The project was abandoned, and in 1851, the ironwork was sold and used for building Brunel's Royal Albert Bridge over the Tamar.

After Brunel's death at the age of 53 in 1859 his colleagues at the Institution of Civil Engineers decided to form a company to complete his project – effectively his memorial – with William Henry Barlow and Sir John Hawkshaw as engineers. Some details were adapted, but broadly Brunel's final plan was adhered to, and the work was completed in 1864. The deck, originally planned to be timber, was instead made of wrought iron, while the towers were left as rough stone and not decorated with the Egyptian decoration as intended. As it happened, Brunel's Hungerford Suspension Bridge (see page 156) was being dismantled and its four chains (two pairs of two) were reused at Clifton – an extra chain was added to each side to provide additional weight. Brunel's plan was a daring, bold solution to spanning the 76-metre (249-foot) deep gorge, and he created a grand design that beautifies the landscape. The bridge is built with no side spans, and the chains are anchored in the rock on each side of the gorge, near the top. The chains pass over roller-mounted 'saddles' positioned on the tops of the towers and are allowed to move and so absorb force of the movement of the chains, thus minimising possibility of damage to the towers.

The construction required the building of a temporary bridge, with six wire ropes stretched across the gorge, to create a footbridge with handrails, plank footway and an overhead wire by means of which a wheeled frame was attached to carry each link of the chain. The whole structure was anchored by ropes attached to rocks below. Then vertical suspension rods were bolted to the chains, and girders added to provide rigidity for the deck.

The Clifton Suspension Bridge admirably copes with some 12,000 motor vehicles a day, although it was designed for much lighter traffic. It continues to be financed by tolls charged for vehicles.

CLIFTON STORIES

In the past, bridge has had a notorious reputation as a spot for suicides. Since 1998, barriers have been installed on the bridge to prevent jumping after 127 people were recorded to have plunged to their deaths from here between 1974 and 1993. In 1885, one who freakishly survived was 22-year old Sarah Ann Henley who had an argument with her lover and leapt into the Gorge, but her crinoline dress and petticoats billowed out parachute-fashion and she survived to live another 63 years. In 1957, in flagrant breach of RAF rules, Flying Officer J. G. Crossley flew a Vampire Jet at 720kph (450 mph) under the bridge, crashed into the cliffs and was killed. On 26 November 2003, the very last Concorde flight flew over the bridge before landing at Filton Airfield to mark Bristol's engineering feats.

Name	Clifton Suspension Bridge
Location	Clifton, UK
Crosses	Clifton Gorge
Type	Chain suspension bridge
Function	Road bridge
Main span	214m (702ft)
Total length	414m (1,358ft)
Deck width	9.5m (31ft)
Clearance	76m (249ft) (above high water)
Completed	1864
Designer	Isambard Kingdom Brunel
Participant	William Henry Barlow

TELFORD AND STEPHENSON'S BRIDGES IN NORTH WALES

NORTH WALES / UNITED KINGDOM

Completing the crucial road and rail links to the Irish Sea ferry port of Holyhead presented twin challenges for 19th-century bridge builders – to cross the river at Conwy and the Menai Strait between the mainland and the Isle of Anglesey. Pioneering solutions came from Thomas Telford with his two road suspension bridges and from Robert Stephenson with the tubular rail bridges solution.

TELFORD'S SUSPENSION BRIDGES

Thomas Telford's career as a road builder notably included his road from London to the Irish Sea port of Holyhead, much of it forming the modern A5. Dating from 1826, his two supremely graceful iron suspension bridges in this part of Wales are among the very first road suspension bridges in the world. Their success led to a surge of enthusiasm for suspension bridges.

While building the London to Holyhead Road Telford was approached to take on the Conwy Bridge as part of improvements to the route from Bangor to Chester. His original plan was to erect a cast-iron bridge, but eventually he created the eye-catching Conwy Suspension Bridge. At first sight it seems to be part of 13th-century Conwy Castle, as it is carefully matched up stylistically with the turrets of the formidable medieval structure which it immediately adjoins. It would be an unthinkable act today, but parts of the castle – now a designated World Heritage Site – were demolished to create anchor points for suspension cables. The bridge is owned by the National Trust; visitors can also see inside the toll-keeper's house.

The wider Menai Strait required much larger structures to cross it. Telford's Menai

Left Now flanked by a modern road bridge and a tubular rail bridge designed by Robert Stephenson, the Conwy Suspension Bridge is now only open to pedestrians visiting the Conwy Castle.

Name	Conwy Suspension Bridge
Location	Conwy, Wales
Crosses	Conwy River
Type	Cast-iron suspension
Function	Road bridge
Main span	99.7m (327ft)
Width of deck	2.5m (8.2ft)
Completed	1826
Design	Thomas Telford

Bridge was part of his London to Holyhead road. Hollow towers of local limestone were erected either side of the Strait and joined by 16 chain cables to support the 177-metre central span. To prevent the iron from rusting after it had been produced in Shrewsbury and before it was erected, it was immersed in warm linseed oil. Its wooden deck was replaced in 1893 with a steel surface, and in 1940 the iron chains were replaced with steel, but otherwise it retains much of its original appearance.

STEPHENSON'S IRON BRIDGES

Next to Conwy Suspension Bridge, Stephenson's Conwy Bridge of 1849 crosses the river, carrying the North Wales coast railway line, and like the suspension bridge gets something of the pastiche medieval treatment, with stone abutments at each end built like medieval crenellated turrets. Between them, rather incongruously, runs a rectangular iron box made of wrought-iron plates riveted together, in which the trains are enclosed – a design known as a tubular bridge. This was the innovation of Robert Stephenson, son of the great railway engineer George Stephenson, who built the first successful steam locomotive. The concept, based on shipbuilding techniques, was simple but revolutionary, and is considered the forerunner of the plate girder bridge design that followed much later. During construction the entire 'tube' was floated on to the river and jacked up into position by means of hydraulic pumps.

When the railway was built to Holyhead, the original proposal for crossing the Menai Strait was cumbersome in the extreme, involving uncoupling carriages as they reached the Strait, drawing them across a bridge by horse power, and attaching them to a waiting locomotive on the far side. Stephenson's design for a crossing of the Strait took its name from Britannia Rock, on which one of the piers was placed. Stephenson's Britannia Bridge was like its smaller cousin in Conwy built on the tubular principle, but there was appreciable doubt as to whether a design of this length would be rigid and strong enough to carry heavy trains. He was assisted by two prominent consultant engineers: Eaton Hodgkinson, who took the orthodox and established view that tubes would not be rigid enough and would need suspended chains to bear them, and William Fairbairn who said chains were unnecessary. Stephenson sided with Fairbairn, and a 23-metre (75.5-foot) span model was made and tested at Fairbairn's shipyard in Millwall. The construction techniques of this and the Conwy Bridge influenced Brunel in his approach to building the Royal Albert Bridge (page 133).

In 1970, boys playing on the bridge accidentally dropped a piece of lit paper they were using as a torch, and the whole structure caught fire. It was the end of Stephenson's masterpiece; only the piers remain today. They are still in use to support the replacement double-deck steel truss arch bridge of the same name which opened in 1971 and now carries the A55 above the railway track, which is supported by arches. Beneath the level of the road deck, and out of sight, four 4-metre (13.1-foot) high limestone lions that once proudly adorned the original bridge now crouch in forlorn obscurity.

Name	Britannia Bridge
Location	Near Bangor, Wales
Crosses	Menai Strait
Type	Tubular rail bridge, replaced by road and rail bridge
Main span	Two 146-metre (479-foot) spans
Total length	432m (1,417ft)
Completed	1850 (replaced in 1971)
Design	Robert Stephenson, with assistance from William Fairbairn

Below Similar in construction to the Britannia Bridge, Stephenson also built the wrought iron tubular Conwy Bridge which was completed in 1848. Today it is open only to pedestrians.

Name	Conwy Bridge
Location	Conwy, Wales
Crosses	Conwy River
Type	Tubular railway bridge
Main span	125m (410ft)
Completed	1848 (opened 1849)
Design	Robert Stephenson

Above Robert Stephenson's Britannia Bridge took two years to construct between 1848 and 1850. It was destroyed by fire in 1971 but the remaining piers were incorporated into the new structure.

Right Thomas Telford's Menai Straits Bridge is considered to be the first modern suspension bridge. The original wooden deck and the iron chains were both replaced with steel in 1893 and 1938 respectively.

Name	Menai Straits Bridge
Location	Near Bangor, Wales
Crosses	Menai Strait between Gwynedd and Anglesey
Type	Chain suspension bridge
Main span	177m (580ft)
Total length	521m (1,709ft)
Completed	1826
Designer	Thomas Telford

ROYAL ALBERT BRIDGE

SALTASH / **UNITED KINGDOM**

This bowstring suspension rail bridge (total length 667 metres) is represents one of Brunel's most ingenious creations, and deftly tackled the problem of the Cornwall Railway crossing the Tamar River, while giving a clear headway for naval ships at all times.

BRUNEL'S FINAL CHALLENGE

Towards the end of his life Isambard Kingdom Brunel took on the challenging task of designing a railway bridge that was to put Cornwall on the railway map of Britain. The lie of the land threw up numerous problems. In particular, there was nowhere to secure tension chains, so the bridge has self-supporting lens-shaped (lenticular) arch trusses, placed on top of the piers. A single pier mid-stream supports two spans, with a further ten approach spans on the Cornwall side and seven on the Devon side.

Supported by three piers and formed of two spans, the central part of the bridge comprises tubular 'bowstring' arches in the form of parabolas. These are made of curved tubes of wrought-iron plates that were riveted together on the shore and then floated out to be jacked into position – a technique inspired by the construction a few years earlier of Stephenson's tubular rail bridges on the Menai Strait and at Conwy (see pages 128-131). The construction of the central pier was a major challenge for Brunel, since there was no suitable islet to build it on. His solution was to float out an airtight pneumatic cylinder, or caisson, in which workmen could excavate into the bedrock. Here he adapted the concept of a diving shield that his father Marc Brunel, also an engineer, had patented, and used for the construction of the Thames Tunnel (1843). Up to 40 men could work underwater in the caisson at any one time.

CONSTRUCTION AS SPECTACLE

Huge crowds came to see the spans brought out. The floating out of the first truss in September 1857 drew some 20,000 spectators. The procedure involved a workforce of 500 to manoeuvre them into position; the truss was then raised on jacks at a rate of two metres (6.6ft) a week. Special trains from London brought sightseers to witness the positioning of the second truss in July 1858. Brunel, however, was not there to enjoy the spectacle: too unwell to attend, he only once saw his completed bridge, opened in 1859 by Prince Albert, when he travelled across in an open wagon shortly before his death.

Name	Royal Albert Bridge
Location	Saltash, UK
Crosses	River Tamar
Type	Bowstring suspension bridge
Function	Railway bridge
Length	667m (2,188ft)
Main spans	Two 177-metre (455-foot) spans
Clearance	30m (98ft)
Opened	1859
Design	Isambard Kingdom Brunel

BRICK RAILWAY VIADUCTS

In Britain's railway age, bricks became increasingly used for building, and mass-production of bricks went hand in hand with industrial expansion in many parts of the country. Some of the grandest structures of the period were brick railway viaducts and ironically the new railways spelt the demise of the waterways along which the bricks themselves were often transported. Britain's numerous brick viaducts strode across rural and urban landscapes. The London and Greenwich Railway (built 1836–38, and the first railway anywhere built specifically for passengers) runs 6 kilometres (3.7 miles) over 878 low brick arches built of 60 million bricks, avoiding the need for level crossings.

Many of those who travel on the railway from London to Brighton are oblivious to the moment near Balcombe when the train crosses over the 37-arch Ouse Valley Viaduct which, at 29m (95ft) high and 450m (1,476ft) long, is one of the most spectacular railway monuments in the country, and a remarkable embellishment of the green Sussex countryside. It was built in 1841 with John Rastrick as the chief engineer, with a classical balustrade along its entire length, and fanciful stone pavilions at either end. The design used 11 million bricks and saved many more by virtue of the fact that each of its piers is built with a huge oval cut-out void in the middle – offering an extraordinary effect of perspective to anyone who walks underneath and looks through all the spaces along the length of the structure.

Below The 37 graceful arches of the Balcombe Viaduct stretch across the Ouse Valley, and still carries trains on the main London to Brighton rail line.

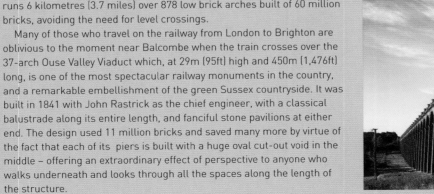

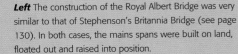

Left The construction of the Royal Albert Bridge was very similar to that of Stephenson's Britannia Bridge (see page 130). In both cases, the mains spans were built on land, floated out and raised into position.

TOWER BRIDGE

LONDON / **UNITED KINGDOM**

The most famous and complex bascule bridge ever built, Tower Bridge has a strange hybrid form and is one of London's most iconic structures, representing the city's eastern gateway and evoking its heyday as a port.

CROSSING THE THAMES

As the Port of London expanded during Victorian times and the population grew with it, there became an urgent need to provide an alternative river crossing in this area of the capital. London Bridge was extremely congested, and there was no bridge further east. The idea of a bridge crossing here goes back to 1824 when a proposal was made to build a bridge with iron chains between stone piers, 24m (78.7ft) above the water, but nothing came of the project. In 1870, the Tower Subway, the world's first underground railway, opened beneath the Thames 400m (1,312ft) west of the present site of Tower Bridge, but it was hardly sufficient and closed later that year.

A parliamentary Bill in 1872 sought authority to build a 'tower bridge' between Tower Hill and Southwark. As this would be in the midst of the port area, the design had to avoid disrupting river traffic. Various schemes, some highly fanciful,

were submitted to the Bridge House Estates Committee. These included a tunnel, a floating chain bridge, a Paddle Wheel Ferry Bridge, a High-Level Bridge with hydraulic lifts to convey horses and carriages to the top of each of two towers and onto the bridge, and a Low-Level Bridge, which divided into two separate carriageways, each with its own swing bridge, to allow road traffic to cross one bridge as shipping was passing through the other.

OPENING SPAN

Ultimately, Parliament ruled that the bridge erected here would require an opening span. In 1876 the City of London Corporation, responsible for this stretch of river (as it still is to this day), ran an open competition to find a bridge design. The chosen entry was by Horace Jones (1819–1887), the City's own architect and designer of Smithfield Market. His design superficially resembles the final structure; it detailed a low-level opening bascule bridge (bascule being from the

Right New rules and signals had to be developed for river traffic passing through the bridge; a combination of red semaphore signals for day and coloured lights at night. A gong was used in foggy weather.

French word for seesaw) with two turreted Gothic towers between a semicircular span, which opened by means of massive chains much like the drawbridge of a castle. However, this did not give enough clearance for ships, though its Gothic appearance was deemed suitably dignified and apt for London's gateway, close as it was to the Tower of London.

THE REVISED PLAN

With the assistance of the engineer Sir John Wolfe Barry, the scheme was adapted to the design of bridge that opened in 1894, seven years after Jones's death. In this revised plan the two Gothic towers, clad in Cornish granite and Portland stone are built around a steel frame supported by two huge piers. They house internal hydraulics, originally powered by steam turbines, which take around one minute to lift the bascules to an angle of 83 degrees in order to allow river traffic to pass. The energy required to achieve the lift is stored in six massive accumulators which feed the driving engines. Since 1976 the hydraulics have been driven by oil and electricity.

Left Tower Bridge is crossed by more than 40,000 pedestrians and motorists a day. The bridge is still raised around 1,000 times a year; whilst river traffic is now much reduced, it still takes priority over road traffic.

Two high-level walkways, 42m (138ft) above the river at high tide and accessed by lifts, originally provided access for pedestrians so that they would not have to wait for the bridge to close before crossing. They were closed to the public in 1910 through lack of use – people apparently preferred to wait and enjoy the spectacle of the bridge opening. The footways were cantilevered from each tower for 17m (55.8ft), with suspended girders used to bridge the remaining 36.5m (128ft) between each cantilever end. The side spans are suspension bridges and at street level.

ICON OR EYESORE?

The bridge undeniably retains a huge public affection, but its aesthetics have been questioned by engineers and others – for its outmoded Gothic details, and for the clumsy, drooping trusses that support the side spans. The artist Frank Brangwyn (1867–1956) stated that 'a more absurd structure than the Tower Bridge was never thrown across a strategic river'. In the midst of the Second World War, one W. F. C. Holden, the architect of the National Provincial Bank, proposed a bizarre scheme for the bridge when the war was over; to surround the entire structure with glass – with bright, large-windowed offices looking down on the river – thereby eliminating need for painting and maintenance, and presumably also

covering up what Holden regarded as a Victorian eyesore.

THE TOURIST BRIDGE

Today the bridge continues to be lifted approximately 1,000 times a year for large craft such as naval vessels and cruise ships. The high-level walkways were glazed in and reopened in 1982 and now form a museum about the bridge itself, along with the interior of the towers; Visitors can see the original steam turbines, plans of various designs of the bridge and take a tour of the present-day workings. Since the opening of the Queen Elizabeth II Bridge between Dartford and Thurrock in 1991, Tower Bridge is no longer the most easterly span on the River Thames.

Name	Tower Bridge
Location	London
Crosses	River Thames
Type	Bascule and suspension
Purpose	Road traffic bridge
Main span	79m (259ft)
Side spans	82m (270ft)
Clearance	8.5m (28ft), 42m (138ft) when opened
Completion	1884
Architect	Sir Horace Jones
Engineer	John Wolfe-Barry

TOWER BRIDGE STORIES

Tower Bridge is often confused with London Bridge and this has led to a popular urban myth surrounding the structure. It is true that John Rennie's London Bridge of 1831 was shipped piece-by-piece to Lake Havasu City, Arizona following its purchase by the American entrepeneur Robert McCulloch but his belief that he had actually bought the more well-known Tower Bridge is without foundation. The bridge was sold by the City of London after it was no longer able to take the increased traffic flows of modern London. It was reconstructed in Arizona between 1968 and 1971 and like its former counterpart, Tower Bridge, is a popular tourist attraction, albeit on the other side of the world.

However, other famous tales are true. One involves a crowded 78 bus bound for Dulwich, South London, one December evening in 1952. The bus was actually on Tower Bridge as the roadways began to open. With great presence of mind, the driver pressed down the accelerator and the bus jumped the small but rapidly widening gap before it would have been too late to reverse.

In 1968, a Hawker Hunter jet fighter made an unauthorised flight under the bridge's walkway after flying at low level down the Thames (and past the Houses of Parliament). The pilot, Flt Lt Al Pollock, was arrested upon landing and discharged from the RAF.

FORTH RAIL BRIDGE

QUEENSFERRY / **UNITED KINGDOM**

When the Forth Bridge was built it shattered many records: for the largest volumes of masonry and steel ever used in a bridge as well as for the highest, longest, deepest and most widely-spanning cantilevers. The immensity of this structure, still one of the world's largest and most famous bridges, owes much to the example of the Tay Bridge disaster which took place only a few years before on the same rail route.

MARGIN OF STRENGTH
The great estuaries of the Forth, at Edinburgh, and the Tay, near Dundee, were huge natural obstacles in the way of a continuous west coast railway for Scotland; passengers on the North British line had to break their journeys for lengthy ferry crossings which were often cancelled in rough weather.

The catastrophic failure of Sir Thomas Bouch's Tay Bridge in 1879 (see page 141) led to his design for a giant Forth suspension bridge being abandoned, even though a foundation stone had already been laid. The newly appointed designers,

Sir John Fowler and Benjamin Baker, were hugely aware of the need for strength and stiffness in their own structure. They specified that it should withstand more than five times the wind pressure allowed for under the previous plan. Although this was excessive for the needs of the time, it gave the bridge a margin of strength that made it well able to cope with the increasing weight of railway traffic that was forecast into the 20th century.

THE CANTILEVER PRINCIPLE
Since the Firth of Forth is up to 65m (213ft) deep, it would have been unfeasible to build the numerous piers that would have

Right The construction of the bridge used natural features to support the steel structure wherever possible, including using the island of Inchgarvie, the promontories on either side of the firth and the high banks at either side.

Name	Forth Rail Bridge
Location	Queensferry, UK
Crosses	Firth of Forth
Type	Cantilever bridge
Function	Railway bridge
Span	Two 521-metre (1,709ft) spans
Length	2.46km (1.5 miles)
Height	100.6m (330ft)
Clearance	45.7m (150ft)
Opened	1890
Design	Sir John Fowler and Benjamin Baker

Left In 1996, a £40 million refurbishment of the bridge made repairs to the steelwork, surface coating, improvements to access and an upgrade of the bridge's floodlighting.

been needed for a series of truss spans like the Tay Bridge. Fowler and Baker instead brought in two notable innovations – the use of steel and the cantilever principle. Steel (rather than cast iron) was first used for a major bridge at St Louis (1874) but remained unauthorised in Britain until the Forth Bridge. The earliest modern cantilever bridge was built over the Main in Germany by Heinrich Gerber in 1867, and a number were under construction in the US, but the design was unprecedented in Britain. In a famous demonstration, Baker illustrated the principle using two seated men supporting a visiting engineering student from Japan on a board, using only their outstretched arms and sticks to represent the piers, cantilevers and suspended span.

THE GOLDEN RIVET

Construction began in 1883 with the three great piers, at North and South Queensferry and on the midriver islet of Inchgarvie; each pier consisting of four 21.3-metre (69.9-foot) circular pads, filled with stone rubble and

faced with granite. The cantilever arms were built out simultaneously from the steel towers to balance the forces involved, while the viaducts that approach the cantilevered part of the bridge are on the scale of major bridges in their own right. Up to 4,000 workmen were employed at a time and some six and a half million rivets were used – the last, a 'golden rivet', formally tapped into place by Edward, Prince of Wales on 4 March, 1890. To some, the design was shockingly stark and functional: the Arts and Crafts designer, critic and poet William Morris described it as 'the supremest specimen of all ugliness'.

PAINTING THE FORTH BRIDGE

A popular term for a never-ending task is 'painting the Forth Bridge', based on the belief that at one time as soon as one repainting was finished, work started again at the other end, though the truth of this is now disputed. Today, however, it is maintained with high-specification modern paints with a 20-year lifespan.

THE TAY BRIDGE DISASTER

The first Tay Bridge went into service in 1878 securing Thomas Bouch, engineer to the North British railway company, a knighthood. Already a distinguished railway engineer, he had created what was at the time the longest bridge in the world, a massive wrought-iron viaduct, 3.26 kilometres (2 miles) long, with a central section of trussed spans (the 'high girders') through which the trains ran to give shipping greater clearance in the centre of the Firth. But, fatally, the high girders were not braced to the rest of the structure, and during a gale in December 1879 they collapsed as a mail train and six coaches were crossing inside the latticework, killing 75 people.

A Court of Inquiry report ruled that Bouch had been dangerously complacent about design, workmanship and maintenance and, most of all, about the need for such a bridge to withstand gusts of intense wind pressure as well as steady forces – although this was not established practice at the time. Work on his suspension bridge for the Firth of Forth was called to a halt, and he died, his health broken, a few months after the report was published.

Below A drawing from the *Illustrated London News* depicts steam launches and a diver's barge searching for bodies and survivors of the Tay Bridge disaster in Dundee.

THE MIDDLESBROUGH TRANSPORTER BRIDGE

MIDDLESBROUGH / **UNITED KINGDOM**

England's sole working example of the transporter bridge – a type also known as the 'ferry bridge' or 'aerial transfer' – carries traffic over the Tees on the A178 between Middlesbrough and Hartlepool. It has very much become a symbol of the industrial town of Middlesbrough.

AN INDUSTRIAL RARITY

Very few bridges of this type have been built anywhere in the world. A moving section of bridge is suspended by cables hanging from steel truss spans between two towers, with steel cables acting as anchor for the cantilevered end spans. The moving section, which often has the feeling of a river boat deck with seats, an awning and a wheelhouse-like control room, is loaded with its cargo and then moved to the other side of the river like a ferry suspended between two tall towers. The number of vehicles that transporter bridges can take is very limited – just nine in the case of the Middlesbrough

bridge – but they can move large numbers of people very efficiently. Transporter bridges also allow for the passage of ships around them, and unlike ferries they can operate around the clock, regardless of the state of the tide. A further advantage is that they do not require the long approach ramps which would be necessary for a high road bridge which enabled ships to pass.

THE RUSH TO THE FERRY

Bilbao's Vizcaya Bridge (see overleaf), which opened in 1893, was the world's first structure of this kind. However, the idea originated more than two decades earlier

Name	Middlesbrough Transporter
Location	Middlesbrough
Crosses	River Tees
Function	Aerial ferry transfer
Materials	Steel
Main span	143m (469ft)
Total length	260m (853ft)
Clearance	49m (160ft)
Completed	1911
Design	Cleveland Bridge & Engineering Co Ltd
Consulting engineer	Georges Camille Imbault

Right As the largest working bridge of its kind in the world, the Middlesbrough Transporter is 225 feet (69 metres) high at its tallest point.

MIDDLESBROUGH TRANSPORTER BRIDGE

in Middlesbrough. The town had grown around a point where the Tees had been forded from early times between communities either side. The river crossing grew more important as the Port Clarence area on the north bank became industrialized, and eventually the ferry services could not cope with the need to transport workers rapidly from one side to the other. Even on a good day, the ferry took 15 minutes to cross the river, in addition to an extra five minutes to allow for embarking and disembarking. This became a source of frustration to the thousands of people who used it, and they would hurry to get to the ferry after their shifts ended; bad weather and adverse tidal conditions frequently exacerbated matters.

SMITH'S PLAN
In 1872 Charles Smith, the manager of the Hartlepool Ironworks, put forward the idea of building a bridge with a span of 198m (650ft) and a headway of 46m (151ft), using the unprecedented aerial ferry or transporter principle and costing £31,162. This, it was proposed, would facilitate the journey for workmen from Middlesbrough to their workplace on the far bank. The corporation did not approve his plan, and opted instead for a larger ferry. However,

Left and Right The bridge is currently a Grade II* listed building and the Institution of Mechanical Engineers has awarded the bridge its highest honour for engineering excellence.

ferries at this point were susceptible to delays, and crossing times were always much longer.

Smith's plan was revisited in 1901 after other bridge designs and a tunnel had been rejected, and six years later the Corporation put through a parliamentary Bill to erect a transporter bridge to replace the ferry. The contract was signed, stipulating a 27-month construction period and a cost of precisely £68,026 6s 8d (although that was eventually exceeded). When it finally opened in 1911, the Middlesbrough Transporter Bridge was instantly hailed as an engineering triumph, enabling workers to cross in just two and a half minutes.

VIZCAYA BRIDGE
Ferdinand Arnodin adopted Charles Smith's concept and opened the Vizcaya Bridge in Bilbao in 1893. Designated a UNESCO World Heritage Site, it runs every eight minutes, 24 hours a day, is 164m (538ft) long and can transport 80 tonnes – six cars and several dozen passengers in a minute and a half. In France five such bridges were erected, more than any other country, while two have been built in the United States. In the UK, the 1905 Runcorn-Widnes Transporter Bridge spanned 305m (1,001ft) across the Mersey and was demolished in the early 1960s; the Newport Transporter Bridge in Wales was constructed across the Usk in 1906 to serve the Orb Steel Works and still stands, spanning 197m (646ft). The longest transporter bridge was built in the Soviet era in Stalingrad (now Volgograd), while that at Rendsburg on the Kiel Canal in Germany is perhaps the most unusual. Built in 1913 and spanning 2,500m (8,202ft), it effectively comprises two bridges in one, with a rail bridge across the top section and a transporter bridge below.

Below The Vizcaya Bridge, despite being the oldest transporter in the world, has only seen one major interruption in service – for four years during the Spanish Civil War, when the upper section was partially destroyed by dynamite.

HUMBER BRIDGE

HUMBER ESTUARY / **UNITED KINGDOM**

At the time the longest suspension span ever built, and crossing
the last great unbridged estuary in Britain, the Humber Bridge
was an engineering triumph which fulfilled a century-old need
– yet due to an accident of timing it has yet to pay for itself.

Name	Humber Bridge
Location	West of Hull
Crosses	Humber Estuary
Type	Suspension bridge
Function	Road, pedestrian and cycle
Main span	1,410m (4,626ft)
Length	2,220m (7,283ft)
Clearance	30m (98ft)
Height	155m (510ft)
Opened	17 July 1981
Design	Freeman Fox and Partners

LOCAL CAMPAIGN

For more than 100 years, Hull businesses
had campaigned for a bridge or tunnel
across the Humber Estuary to reduce their
dependence on the ferry crossing. Final
approval for a suspension bridge came in
1959 with the Humber Bridge Act, though
work did not begin until 1971 and the bridge
did not open for a further decade. It held
the world record for the longest single span
suspension bridge for 17 years until 1998,
when it was overtaken by the Great Belt
and Akashi-Kaikyo bridges (pages 52
and 186). It was also the first long-span
suspension bridge to have its towers built
of concrete. Each pair of hollow vertical
columns tapers from 6m² (19.7ft²) at the
base to 4.5m x 4.75m (14.8ft x 15.6ft) at
the top.

BENEFITS TO THE AREA

The Humber Bridge vastly improved
communications between two remote parts
of England. Previously a 20-minute ferry
crossing had carried 90,000 vehicles a year
and a brief experiment with a hovercraft
crossing in 1968 had proved unreliable.
Today more than 100,000 vehicles cross
the bridge each week. However, this is
only about a quarter of the traffic using
the two Severn Bridges (see page 148), and
the Humber Bridge has suffered financial
problems, dating back to the high price
inflation, interest rates and delays during
the years it was being built.

COSTLY ENTERPRISE

The cost, originally estimated at £28
million, grew to £98 million, and interest
on the government loans paying for it put
the enterprise in debt by £151 million
before it was even finished. Despite
various concessions from the Treasury, the
construction loans are not expected to be
paid off until 2032, and there is considerable
local discontent about continuing to be
charged tolls for such a long period after
the bridge was completed.

Right The Humber Bridge links Hessle in the north to Barton-upon-Humber in the south. Both previously remote areas
have benefited economically from the construction of the bridge.

SEVERN BRIDGE

SEVERN ESTUARY / UNITED KINGDOM

Providing a direct motorway link between England and South Wales, the Severn Bridge was highly innovative for its time but a vast increase in traffic meant that it first had to be strengthened, then supplemented with a second crossing.

ACROSS AN ESTUARY AND A RIVER

The first Severn crossing consists of two bridges, with the best-known main suspension section spanning the Severn Estuary, whilst the second smaller section, a cable-stayed bridge, crosses the River Wye. They are linked by two box girder viaducts.

The suspension bridge design was influenced by German structural engineer Fritz Leonhardt (1909–1999) who in response to the Tacoma Narrows disaster (see page 213) moved in a radically different direction to the US designers who were installing deep trusses on their suspension bridges to ensure stability in high winds. Instead he developed the idea that a narrow deck with an aerofoil profile to 'cut' the forces of the wind could be just as effective, using considerably less steel as well as being more light and elegant in appearance than the deep trusses. The aerofoil of the Severn Bridge deck, 3m (9.8ft) deep at its centre, is achieved by its tapering to each side and then being flanked by slender foot and cycleways which are cantilevered outwards. The zigzag arrangement of the cables was unusual for the time and was intended to dampen the movement of the structure.

A NEW FUTURE?

Opened by Queen Elizabeth II in September 1966, the bridge was acclaimed as launching a new economic future for South Wales. While its coal and steel industries fared badly in the 1980s and 1990s, the direct motorway, along with good rail links, has linked Cardiff and other parts of South Wales such as Newport and Swansea to the M4 corridor's regional economy stretching through Bristol and Reading to west London.

TRAFFIC PROBLEMS

Even as the Severn Bridge was being built, there were huge changes taking place in Britain's road traffic. Many more goods were being moved in much heavier vehicles. Strengthening and improvement work, including installing extra tubular columns inside each corner of the towers, reinforcing the deck joints and replacing the hangers and replacing the road surface, was carried out between 1986 and 1991. However, congestion at peak holiday and commuting times was becoming severe by this point and in order to alleviate this the M4 Second Severn Crossing, a cable-stayed bridge, was completed some 5 kilometres (3.1 miles) downstream in 1996.

Name	Severn Bridge
Location	Between Aust and Beachley
Crosses	Severn Estuary
Type	Suspension bridge
Function	Road, pedestrian and cycle bridge
Main span	988m (3,240ft)
Length	1,600m (5,249ft)
Clearance	47m (154ft)
Height	136 metres (446ft)
Opened	8 September 1966
Design	Freeman Fox and Partners,. Mott, Hay & Anderson

149

Left When it first opened, the lightweight deck of the Severn Bridge was applauded as a landmark in aerodynamic design. The illuminations are located below platform level to minimise glare for users of the bridge.

GATESHEAD MILLENNIUM BRIDGE

GATESHEAD / UNITED KINGDOM

Opened in 2001 at a cost of £22 million, this unique pivoting structure not only links recently-regenerated areas each side of the Tyne, but enhances its setting as part of a group of historic and closely located bridges, so much so that it has become a significant tourist attraction.

CRITERIA FOR A NEW BRIDGE

Gateshead Council had launched a competition for a new bridge across the river in 1996, which attracted some 150 entries. The designers had to meet tough criteria: the pedestrian and cycle routes had to stay much at the same level as the low riverbanks, and a 30-metre (98.4-foot) wide channel for shipping was required. In addition the design had to complement the other famous Tyne bridges close by, particularly the soaring arch of the 1920s Tyne Bridge and the precarious-looking road and railway tracks borne high above the river by Stephenson's High Level Bridge.

THE EYELID SOLUTION

The solution of architects Wilkinson Eyre was highly original: an eyelid structure that moves on an axis to allow rivercraft to pass underneath. The pair of parabolic steel arches have common anchorages on each side of the bank and are connected at 100 degrees apart by a series of 18 stressed cables. Pedestrian and cycle routes are carried on one arch, while the other vertical arch echoes the shape of the nearby Tyne Bridge. For ships to pass the two arches pivot on their anchorages, powered by six hydraulic rams, until the connecting cables are horizontal and the two arches

Left The Millennium Bridge is located on the quayside close to the Baltic Centre for Contemporary Art (centre), formerly the Baltic Flour Mill. The bridge is just one of the buildings spearheading the redevelopment and regeneration of the area.

GATESHEAD MILLENNIUM BRIDGE

are symmetrically angled. Each tilt takes four minutes, and the design is so energy-efficient that it now costs only a few pounds for each opening.

In November 2000 a giant floating crane, the Asian Hercules II, the largest vessel ever to venture this far up the Tyne, installed the entire 800-tonne structure in one piece during a three-day operation. It fitted into place with a tolerance of just 2 millimetres either way.

REGENERATION

Located close to the shiny stainless-steel structure of the Sage Gateshead and the renovated former flour mill of the Baltic Centre for Contemporary Art, the Millennium Bridge has set the standard for the regeneration of the Gateshead and Newcastle area. It has also won awards from around the world for is design and unique eye-lid appearance, giving rise to the nickname the 'Blinking Eye bridge'. As a leader of Gateshead Council

commented, 'we knew we had something very special… but even though we knew how innovative it was, we have been taken aback by the massive worldwide interest'.

Even the small details are painstakingly thought out. For example, any litter on the bridge is collected automatically into special traps each time the bridge opens. At night the structure is illuminated by lights below the deck and spotlights that vary in colour constantly.

Name	Gateshead Millennium Bridge
Crosses	River Tyne
Type	Cantilever arch bridge
Function	Pedestrian and cycle bridge
Span	105m (345ft)
Length	126m (413ft)
Height	50m (164ft)
Clearance	15m (49ft), 25m (82ft) open
Opened	17 September 2001
Design	Wilkinson Eyre Architects Gifford & Partners

OTHER TYNE BRIDGES

The Tyneside skyline has been described as 'a veritable cacophony of bridges' where seven distinctive crossings can be found within a mile of each other. Historically most were vital to the development of the region's heavy industries of shipbuilding, coal mining and iron and steel working. Closest to the Millennium Bridge is the Tyne Bridge (1928), that inspired the Sydney Harbour Bridge, and was the world's first bridge to span a river with no supports in the water. The Swing Bridge (1876) enables shipping to pass by rotating 90 degrees around a central pivot so that the bridge deck is parallel to the banks, and was the largest opening bridge of its kind when completed. Close by, the High Level bridge (1849) was the first to have a twin deck with a roadway running beneath a railway track. It was designed by Robert Stephenson, son of steam train pioneer

George Stephenson. During the period of 'railway mania' in the mid-19th century, the number of bridges in Britain is estimated to have doubled from around 30,000 to 60,000. The new railway bridges had to cope with an unprecedented heavy moving load, far more than anything pedestrians and road vehicles could present at the time (stone and brick viaducts and cast-iron beams, arches and trusses were selected according to the requirements of the site). The High Level Bridge uses six shallow 'bowstring' arches in cast iron, with the roadway suspended from them with wrought-iron rods. Three further, less distinctive bridges – the King Edward Bridge (1906), the Redheugh Bridge (replaced twice, latest version 1983) and the Queen Elizabeth Metro Bridge (1981) complete the seven.

Gateshead Millennium Bridge

Left A core requirement of the competition brief stipulated that the winning design should complement other bridges and buildings on the Tyne. In fact, the bridge echoes the shape of the nearby Tyne Bridge.

Right The Millennium Bridge is no less spectacular at night when both the arch and the walkway are fully illuminated with coloured lighting. To prevent it from distracting ships, the bridge is not lit when opened.

MILLENNIUM BRIDGE

LONDON / **UNITED KINGDOM**

One of more than 30 footbridges in the United Kingdom erected to mark the beginning of the new millennium, London's sleek Millennium Bridge was the first new span to be built over the Thames in the capital since Tower Bridge in 1894. However, it became most famous for the initial disconcerting sideways movement that caused Londoners to nickname it the 'Wobbly Bridge'.

ART ON THE THAMES

The Millennium Bridge, located between Southwark and Blackfriars bridges, is all about seeing and being seen. It opened up a new pedestrian route from St. Paul's Cathedral to the Tate Modern art gallery, with an impressive vista of St. Paul's from the South Bank, framed by the supports of the bridge. From it extend superb views of central London, and the bridge itself is effectively a public art installation, its unusual design a unique collaboration between engineers Ove Arup, architects Foster and Partners and the sculptor Sir Anthony Caro. This partnership won an

international competition for a new span over the Thames, held in 1996 by the *Financial Times* in conjunction with the London Borough of Southwark and the Royal Institute of British Architects.

MILLENNIUM INNOVATION

The challenge was to create a bridge that could give unimpeded views, and satisfy stringent height restrictions. The solution was boldly innovative, a lightweight aluminium deck with stainless-steel balustrades, supported at each side by exceptionally shallow cables, which sag only 2.3m (7.5ft) over the 144m (472ft) of

155

Left The bridge, which can support a working load of up to 5,000 people at a time, was designed to be a 'blade of light' across the Thames to celebrate London and Britain at the beginning of a new millennium.

MILLENNIUM BRIDGE

the central span – some six times shallower than a conventional suspension bridge – and which are below the pedestrians' sight line. It comprises three main sections supported by two piers in the river, with four suspension cables on each side held by transverse arms and tensioned to pull with a force of 2,000 tonnes against piers set into each bank – a particularly high tension for a bridge of this size. During construction, bales of straw were hung from the bridge, an ancient tradition to warn passing boats. At night it is illuminated at deck level to form what the designers conceived as a 'blade of light' across the river, and it can accommodate up to 5,000 people on the bridge at any one time.

THE SWAY
However, at the much-heralded opening of the bridge on 10 June 2000, an unexpected problem arose. A huge crowd of people turned up for the event. As they slowly made their way across, the whole bridge began to sway perceptibly and people grasped the handrails for support and balance. The number of people allowed on the bridge was then restricted, but two days later the bridge was closed.

Various theories for the sway were considered and rejected – including that the large flags positioned on it for the opening ceremony accompanied by strong winds had caused vibrations. Research carried out by the engineers Ove Arup revealed that the cause was the technical sounding 'synchronous lateral excitation'. Essentially this described the movement of the bridge caused by a mass of pedestrians walking slowly and in a synchronised fashion. This could have resulted from marching in time to the band, and would have been exacerbated by the simultaneous movements of pedestrians to counteract any swaying that was taking place. Such problems had indeed happened elsewhere, such as during a demonstration on Auckland Harbour Bridge, New Zealand, in 1975. However, this issue had not been routinely addressed in bridge-building practices.

RESEARCH AND TESTING
Arup carried out a programme of testing on human gait, on artificially shaking the bridge, on effects of movements of crowds, and on measuring the vibrations of people walking at different speeds. The findings were circulated to other bridge designers.

The eventual solution was to absorb and neutralise the sideways movement with a system of devices placed beneath the deck: 37 energy-dissipating viscous dampers to control horizontal movement and 54 inertial tuned mass dampers which counter any vertical movement. Following a period of testing, the bridge reopened in 2002, and happily the problem has not recurred since.

Name	Millennium Bridge
Location	London
Crosses	River Thames
Type	Suspension footbridge
Main span	144m (472ft)
Side spans	81 and 108m (268 and 354ft)
Total span	325m (1,066ft)
Length	370m (1,214ft)
Deck width	4m (13ft)
Opened	2000, reopened 2002
Design	Foster and Partners, Ove Arup and Sir Anthony Caro

Right Those crossing the bridge from the southern end, near the Globe Theatre and the Tate Modern are presented with a view of the ultimate symbol of London, St Paul's Cathedral, framed by the bridge's supports.

HUNGERFORD BRIDGE AND THE GOLDEN JUBILEE FOOTBRIDGES
In 2002, the year of the Golden Jubilee of Queen Elizabeth II, London gained another pedestrian crossing over the Thames in the form of the Golden Jubilee Footbridges. These flank either side of the graceless Hungerford Bridge, an iron girder rail bridge opened by the South Eastern Railway in 1864 to bring trains across from south London into Charing Cross station. The rail bridge previously had a congested, narrow walkway that nevertheless offered one of the most spectacular viewing platforms in the city. The replacement 4-metre (13-foot) wide footbridges on both sides, now means that pedestrians can now enjoy substantially improved panoramas of the London Eye and the Palace of Westminster.

The original span here was a suspension pedestrian toll bridge (1845) designed by Brunel. When this was replaced by the rail bridge, the chains and suspension elements were ingeniously reused to complete Brunel's Clifton Suspension Bridge in Bristol (see page 124) after his death, while its pair of imposing Italianate towers on either side of the river were demolished. The southern (Surrey) and northern (Middlesex) piers of Brunel's structure still stand.

Lifshutz Davidson and the engineers WSP Group were engaged for the redesign of the footbridge. The work needed to be done without closing the rail bridge, and could not penetrate deep under the riverbed because the Bakerloo Line runs close beneath. Accordingly, the support structure on the northern side was placed on the Victoria Embankment instead of in the river, and the decks were pulled across the river in sections, lifted on to six temporary piers, then raised into position and connected with cable stays suspended from the outward-leaning pylons.

Right During constructions, there were fears of disturbing unexploded bombs on the riverbed. A redesign of the bridge helped to alleviate concerns; the foundations were dug by hand as an extra safety precaution.

AFRICA

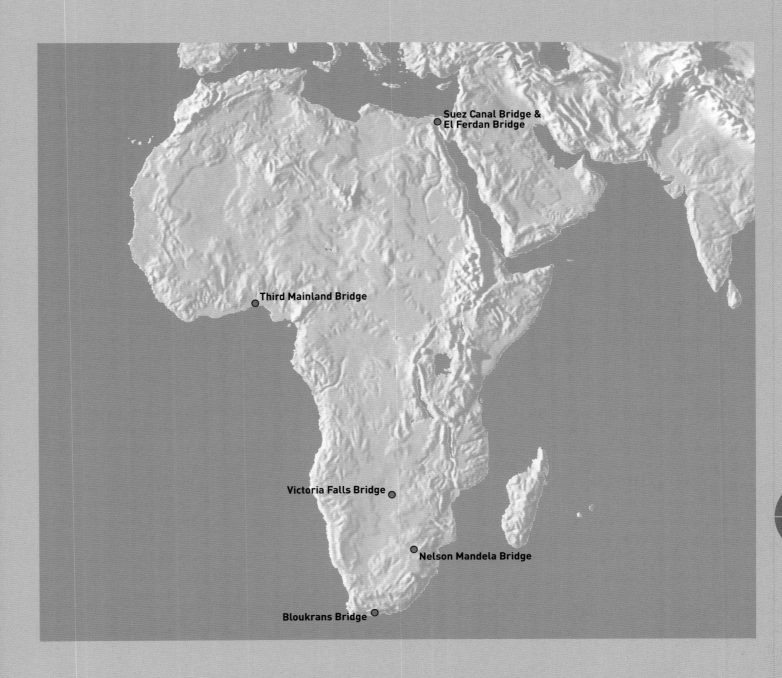

Suez Canal Bridge &
El Ferdan Bridge

Third Mainland Bridge

Victoria Falls Bridge

Nelson Mandela Bridge

Bloukrans Bridge

Left A bungee jumper heads towards the shadow
of the Victoria Falls Bridge on the Zambezi River.

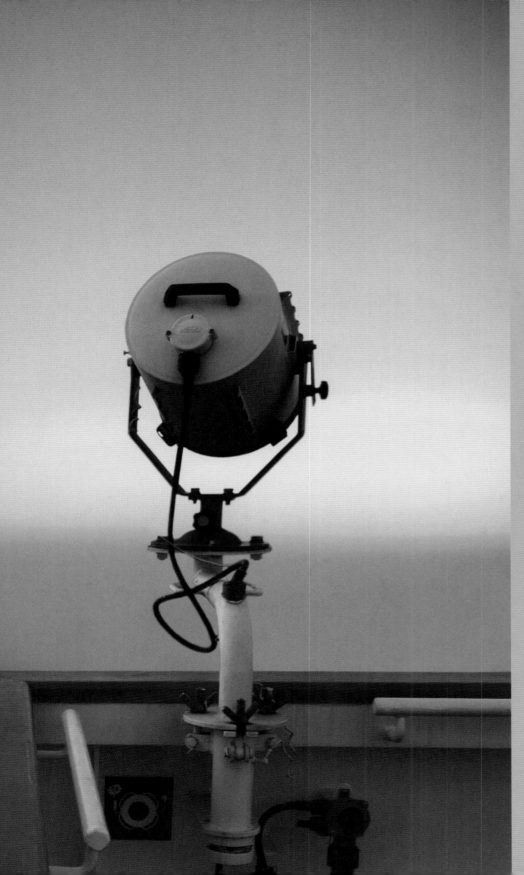

SUEZ CANAL BRIDGE

EL QANTARA / **EGYPT**

Also known as the Japanese-Egyptian Friendship Bridge or the Mubarak Peace Bridge – the Suez Canal Bridge was the first major cable-stayed bridge in Egypt and the Middle East region. This and other crossings over and under the Canal have political significance in their objectives of peace and regional development, and in their improvements of links between Asia and Africa.

STRATEGIC STRUCTURE

The bridge's exceptional height, a clearance of 70m (230ft), is to allow for the Canal's existence as one of the busiest waterways in the world. Opened in 1869 and extending 160km (99.4 miles) from Port Said to Suez, the Canal is capable of accommodating very large vessels of up to 150,000 tonnes and links the Mediterranean and Red Seas, thus forming a strategically important shipping route eastwards from Europe.

INVESTMENT AND DEVELOPMENT

The Canal separates the Sinai Peninsula from the Nile Valley and the rest of Egypt.

The Peninsula's remoteness has meant that it has for long been sparsely settled, and it was contested territory between Egypt and Israel until the Peace Agreement of 1979. An Egyptian government committee, The National Project for the Development of Sinai, has been aiming for the population of the Sinai Peninsula to rise from less than 250,000 in the mid-1990s to a target of nearly 3 million by 2017, with new job opportunities assisted by the al-Salam irrigation canal project, as well as improved access to the area's oil fields and mines. The opening of the bridge and its road link were intended to be a catalyst for economic

161

Left Rising from the flat desert plain, the Suez Canal Bridge dwarfs passing ships and gives motorists a brief but spectacular view over the length of the Suez Canal.

Name	Suez Canal Bridge
Location	El Qantara, Egypt
Crosses	Suez Canal
Type	Cable-stayed bridge
Function	Road bridge
Clearance	70m (230ft)
Length	3.9km (2.4 miles), with side approaches of 1.8km (1.1 miles)
Central span	404m (1,325ft)
Height of pylons	154m (505ft)
Deck width	10m (32.8ft)
Opened	2001

Right Both the piers and the pylons of the Suez Canal Bridge are made of reinforced concrete. The pylons incorporate warning lights for passing aircraft and a system which helps alert engineers of any seismic activity.

expansion alongside other canal-crossing infrastructure projects such as the Ahmed Hamdi Tunnel (1983) and the El Ferdan Bridge (see below).

The construction of the Suez Canal Bridge was a joint venture between the Japanese and Egyptian governments, with 60 per cent of the funding coming from Japan. Its construction was carried out over a 40-month period from 1998 to 2001, by a consortium of Kajima, NKK and Nippon Steel, and with a workforce of 1,000.

CONSTRUCTION

The bridge includes approach sections of 1.8km (1.1 miles) on each side, and a cable-stayed span of 404m (1,325ft) over the Suez Canal itself. This central span is supported by two spectacular 154-metre (505ft) reinforced concrete pylons designed to resemble ancient obelisks which can be seen from the desert far around. Braced by cross beams, each of the two towers is supported by 76 concrete piles which are set 30m (98ft) deep into the ground.

The reinforced concrete for the pylons was created using a round-the-clock slip form system which allows the concrete to be moulded and formed continuously as the structure is built; complex hydraulics and laser beam guidance were used to help to achieve accurate profiles. The pylons incorporate a protection system against damage by lightning, as well as a seismic activity measurement and recording system and navigational warning lights.

EL FERDAN BRIDGE: ANOTHER SUEZ CROSSING

Another key crossing-point on the Suez Canal is the El Ferdan Bridge, the world's largest movable bridge. Opened in 2001, the five-year construction was supervised by the British firm Halcrow. A combined road and rail bridge, it is the fifth to be built on the site since 1920; successive widenings of the canal and destruction of the crossing during conflicts in 1956 and during the 1967 war with Israel have required a series of replacements. The latest structure is a 10,500-tonne double swing bridge, with steel truss structures on each bank, pivoting on 12-metre (39ft) radius bearings to combine to form a span of 340m (1,115ft) with a clearance of 60m (197ft). The design of the new bridge evokes earlier cantilever structures such as the Quebec, Firth and Howrah Bridges, and allows for future plans to widen the waterway further. The El Ferdan Bridge is a link in a new 225-kilometre (140-mile) railway connecting Ismailia with Rafah and like the Suez Canal Bridge, is an integral part of the development of Sinai.

Top The Suez Canal Bridge is also known as the Egyptian-Japanese Friendship Bridge and the Mubarak Peace Bridge (after the President of Egypt – Muhammad Hosni Mubarak).

Above The bridge was built as part of an effort by the Egyptian Government to develop the Sinai Peninsula and encourage people to move out of the densely-populated Nile Valley.

VICTORIA FALLS BRIDGE

VICTORIA FALLS / **ZIMBABWE AND ZAMBIA**

When Cecil Rhodes planned this bridge as part of a proposed Pan-African railway, he expressed his desire that the 'railway should cross the Zambezi just below the Victoria Falls. I should like to have the spray of the falls over the carriages'.

THE PAN-AFRICAN RAILWAY

Rhodes died in 1902 and did not live to marvel at this vertigo-inducing construction, designed to harmonise with the landscape of the gorge and the world's largest waterfall. The bridge was envisioned as part of his never-completed scheme to build a railway across Africa from Cape Town to Cairo. The British Empire had control of an almost continuous stretch of land the length of Africa but disputes between other colonial powers, the worsening world economic situation both before and after the First World War and decline of colonial control meant that the idea was abandoned. The bridge sits on the border of Zambia and

Zimbabwe and as such has border controls at either end; at the towns of Victoria Falls, Zimbabwe and Livingstone in Zambia.

AN AUSTRALIAN CONNECTION

British expertise was instrumental. The construction contract was given to the Cleveland Bridge & Engineering Company of Darlington, while the architect appointed was also British – Sir Ralph Freeman, who later went on to design Sydney Harbour Bridge in Australia (see page 202) and Birchenough Bridge in Zimbabwe. Freeman's steel-arched design, with bracing in the spandrels (the areas between the curves of the arch and the deck) is able to shift

165

Left Taking just over 14 months to build, the Victoria Falls Bridge became central to trade in the country, carrying copper ore and timber out of Zambia and bringing coal into the country.

on steel bearings installed in the concrete abutments, as variations in temperature cause the steelwork to expand or contract.

FORGING AHEAD

Prior to construction a temporary 'Blondin cableway' was placed across the gorge, which was initially spanned by means of a cable attached to a rocket being fired across it. The electrically operated cableway had a conveyor that could move men and materials across for building both the bridge and the railway line on the Zambian side from Livingstone to Kalomo; parts of a locomotive were also moved this way so as to push on with the construction of the railway line to the north. Once across the bridge, they were reassembled for use on the newly built line. Freeman then built out two halves of the steel arch simultaneously from either side of the gorge, tied back by cables anchored into the rock, until they met in the

middle. Safety nets suspended beneath were reportedly removed after insistence from the workers who said their presence made them apprehensive.

VANTAGE POINT

When it was opened as a rail-only bridge in 1905 there were scarcely any motor vehicles in this part of Africa, but the need soon transpired to adapt the bridge to carry a roadway. Accordingly the number of railway lines on the bridge was reduced from two to one, the bridge was widened and strengthened, and a two-lane road and walkway were added in 1930.

A favourite haunt of bungee jumpers, near where the 1.5-km (0.9-miles) wide Zambezi River plummets sheer over a 2-km (1.2-mile) wide basalt cliff and through a series of gorges, the bridge is one of several magnificent vantage points in the vicinity.

Name	Victoria Falls Bridge
Location	Zambia and Zimbabwe
Crosses	Zambezi River
Main span	156.5m (513ft)
Type	Steel arch bridge
Function	Road, rail and pedestrian bridge
Height	128m (420ft)
Completed	1905
Design	Douglas Fox and Partners
Construction	Cleveland Bridge & Engineering Co Ltd
Architect	Sir Ralph Freeman

Right Until recent repairs, the age of the bridge as well as maintenance problems meant restrictions on traffic, including the bridge being closed to heavy vehicles and trains crossing at less than walking pace.

THREE AFRICAN BRIDGES

Another bridge very much on the map of bungee jumpers is Bloukrans Bridge, near Nature's Valley, Western Cape, South Africa, which offers the highest commercially run bungee jump in the world. The 272-metre (892-foot) single-span arch bridge was completed in 1984. It is a giddying 216m (709ft) above the Bloukrans River that forms the border between the Eastern Cape and Western Cape provinces.

An elegantly simple addition to Johannesburg's skyline, Nelson Mandela Bridge is the largest cable-stayed bridge in southern Africa. This is the keystone of the economic rejuvenation project of Johannesburg's inner city, linking the districts of Braamfontein and Newtown. The structure's striking asymmetry is part of its appeal: the two pairs of tubular concrete-filled pylons rise 42 and 27m (138 and 89ft) respectively. The 176-metre (577-foot) central span crosses 42 railway lines and is designed to minimise weight, using structural steel with a concrete composite deck, counterbalanced by heavier reinforced concrete back spans. It rests on gigantic 1.5-metre (4.9-foot) pot bearings - which allow the bridge to contract and expand in the heat. The South African Institute of Civil Engineers judged it 'the most outstanding civil engineering project achievement in the technical excellence category'.

The Third Mainland Bridge is one of three that connect mainland Nigeria to Lagos Island. Completed in 1990 to carry road traffic, it is Africa's longest bridge, with a total length of 10.5km (6.5 miles). However, all does not seem well; in 2002 a report observed that the bridge was already suffering from structural problems and that concerns about

vibrations were justified. The road surface on the deck had become uneven and the supporting piers had shifted. It sent alarm bells around the civil engineering world that such a recently completed structure was in such danger. In 2007 the government banned heavy vehicles from using the bridge and lowered the speed limit in a bid to avoid collapse.

Below Named for the great South African leader, the Nelson Mandela Bridge is a striking landmark that includes two lanes of traffic, a cycle path and two footpaths with a continuous toughened glass parapet to ensure the safety of pedestrians.

ASIA

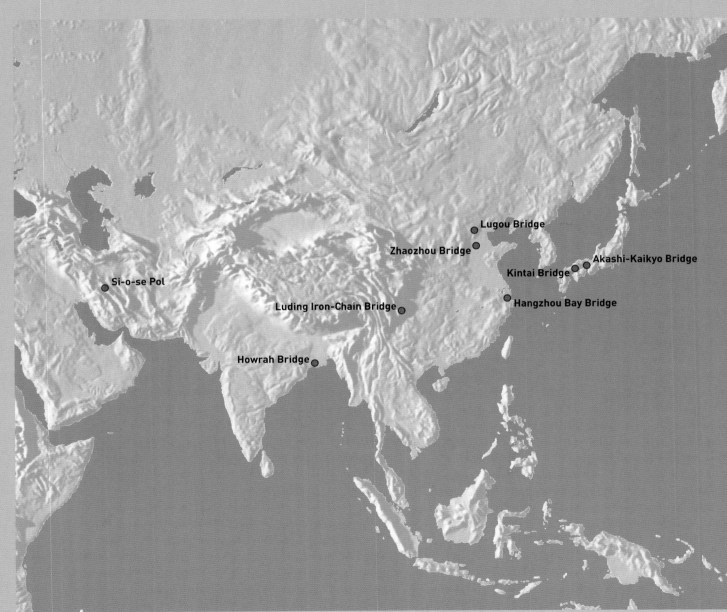

Lugou Bridge

Zhaozhou Bridge

Akashi-Kaikyo Bridge

Kintai Bridge

Si-o-se Pol

Hangzhou Bay Bridge

Luding Iron-Chain Bridge

Howrah Bridge

Left Bathers gather by the Hooghly River in Kolkata, India, alongside the Howrah Bridge.

LUDING IRON-CHAIN BRIDGE

SICHUAN PROVINCE / **CHINA**

In 1935, the 18th-century iron chain bridge in the small market town of Luding was the scene of an incident that became part of the founding legend of modern China – the story of the Long March.

THE IRON-CHAIN BRIDGE

The bridge at Luding is believed to have been constructed by bridge-builders from Tianquanzhou, who were renowned for making iron chains. It formed an important link between Sichuan Province and Tibet, and by the 1930s was still the only crossing of the Dadu River for hundreds of kilometres.

Thirteen iron chains make up the structure, nine forming a floor covered with planking 2.8m (9ft) wide, and two on each side acting as hand rails. The chains are anchored to a stone abutment on each bank. A plaque with the bridge's name, dating from the time of its construction (1705–1706) under Emperor Kangxi, survives at one end of the bridge, and there are temple-style gabled wooden gateways and decorative features at each entrance.

BRIDGE OF SURVIVAL

The Long March was a massive military retreat during the Chinese Civil War made by the Red Army of the Chinese Communist Party between 1934 and 1936. In order to secure the vital river crossing at Luding, a small party of 22 Red Army fighters took the iron chain bridge, clambering across burning and missing planks whilst under machine-gun fire from the opposing Nationalist forces. As a result, the army was able to survive against the odds in the region. More recent accounts dispute the extent of the 'battle' but there is no doubt of the skill and courage of those who crossed the precarious chains under enemy fire.

ANCIENT CHAIN AND SUSPENSION BRIDGES

Iron chain bridges with planking laid across parallel chains are thought to have developed in the mountainous area of Yunnan Province in China more than 2,000 years ago. They provided a solution to spanning deep gorges in the same way as the Inca suspension bridges made of twisted fibre ropes (see pages 252–253) – though each type of bridge evolved completely independently, as a similar solution to a similar environment. Iron chains are also recorded to have been used to block one of the Yangtze River gorges to shipping during a war in AD280.

All of these bridges were prone to twisting and swaying when subject to moving loads. A visitor to Peru as late as the 1870s recorded how travellers would time their journeys to avoid the daily windy periods. China's Ji-hong Bridge in Yunnan Province, dating in its present form from about 1475, though claimed to have origins in the 3rd century AD, is the first ancient suspension bridge known to have used a stiffening mechanism. This consisted of additional chain stays radiating from towers to points along the deck – a precursor of today's cable-stayed bridges.

Name	Luding Iron-Chain Bridge
Location	Luding, Sichuan Province
Crosses	Dadu River
Type	Chain suspension bridge
Function	Pedestrian bridge
Span	104m (341ft)
Clearance	14 metres (46ft)
Opened	1706

Right Known for its role in Long March, in the 19th century the bridge also saw the defeat of the Taiping peasant rebels who would later inspire Mao Zedong.

ZHAOZHOU BRIDGE

SOUTHWEST OF SHIJIAZHUANG, HEBEI PROVINCE / CHINA

Also known as the Safe Crossing Bridge, the Great Stone Bridge or the Anji Bridge, this is the world's oldest open-spandrel segmental arch bridge, and China's oldest bridge of any kind. It was described during the Ming Dynasty as 'a long rainbow hanging on a mountain waterfall'.

SOPHISTICATED STRUCTURE

Remarkably, for a bridge built 1,400 years ago, the name of the builder has survived for posterity. A recently discovered tablet, now placed on a pier, states it was built by the craftsman Li Chun. Another inscription placed by officials of the Tang Dynasty, some 70 years after Zhaozhou Bridge was built, praises Li Chun's ingenious construction, his precision of the fitting of wedge-shaped stones, and the width of the span. Simply way ahead of its time, the bridge spawned many imitations across the country and it has withstood numerous earthquakes, floods and wars that other structures around it have not. Its survival is a testament to the level of sophistication that Chinese engineering had reached some 1,400 years ago, long before any such techniques had reached other parts of the world.

ROBUST DESIGN

Li Chun was instructed to build a structure high and robust enough to avoid flooding and flat and broad enough to allow use by the Imperial Army and for trade caravans, so that carriages and pedestrians could use it simultaneously. Until then stone bridge spans took the form of a semicircle. Here he invented the segmental form – the top quarter segment of a circle rather than a complete semicircle, which comprises 28 curved limestone slabs that are joined with iron dovetails and can be repaired separately. On either side are two smaller arches, or open spandrels, that alleviate the impact of high-level flood water and dispensed with the need for some 700 tonnes of stone, reducing the total weight by 15 per cent; overall the design requires 40 per cent less material than a conventional arched bridge. The entire structure is immensely solid, and has subsided less than 5 centimetres during its entire lifetime; it is not known how Li Chun achieved such accuracy with his weight estimates and engineers still wonder at his precision.

The balustrades of the bridge are decorated with magnificently intricate and individually carved dragons and other mythical creatures, that are believed to guard the bridge and local people against natural disasters such as floods and drought.

BLUEPRINT FOR THE WEST

Other segmental-arch bridges later appeared in China, such as the 6-metre (19.7-foot) long Yongtong Bridge, near Zhaoxian in Hebei, built in 1130. It was many hundreds of years, however, before the design reached the West: the 37-metre (121-foot) span was the longest single arch in the world when it was built, and the longest one in China until the mid-20th century.

AN IMMORTAL CONSTRUCTION?

According to fable, the bridge was built overnight by a master architect named Lu Ban. Two immortals, Chai Rong and Zhang Guolao, crossed the bridge at the same time, Chai Rong wheeling a wheelbarrow loaded with five mountains and Zhang Guolao on his donkey and carrying the sun and moon on his back. Seeing the structure wobble under this immense weight, Lu Ban saved it by leaping into the water and holding up the structure. The bridge supposedly bears depictions of these immortals' imprints – namely the grooves left by the wheelbarrow and the hoof prints of the donkey.

LUPU BRIDGE

Another great Chinese arch appeared in 2003 in the form of the Lupu Bridge over the Huangpu River at Shanghai, providing a massive boost to the city's image and infrastructure. The bow-like arch of this cantilever construction has the biggest span in the world; it outstripped the previous record holder – the New River Gorge Bridge in West Virginia, USA – by 32m (105ft). It is also the world's first completely welded bridge, and contains 35,000 tonnes of steel. During its construction, the two arches were cantilevered and tied to temporary steel towers; in its complete form 27 transverse box structures brace the arches. The design enables it to stand up to natural disasters. The Lupu Bridge can survive an earthquake of 7.0 on the Richter scale, or a hurricane of force 12. It towers over the site of the 2010 Expo, and visitors can take an elevator up to a viewing platform. It takes its name from the two districts it joins – Luwan and Pudong.

Right Stretching 550m (1,804ft) across the river, the Lupu Bridge was constructed with visitors as well as motorists in mind with a basketball court-sized viewing platform affording breathtaking views across Shanghai.

Name	Zhaozhou Bridge
Location	Hebei Province
Crosses	Jiao River
Length	50m (164ft)
Central span	37m (121ft)
Width	9.6m (32ft)
Built	AD596–605
Design	The stonemason Li Chun

Right Remarkable as much for its amazing survival as for its elegant symmetry, the support structure for the Zhaozhou Bridge stands unchanged after 1400 years. Only the ornamented railings have been replaced.

HANGZHOU BAY BRIDGE

HANGZHOU BAY / CHINA

Described by one Chinese observer as a 'money line', this new bridge across the Hangzhou Bay is expected to help to develop the Greater Shanghai economic area into one of the world's sixth-largest urban zones after Paris, London, New York, Tokyo and Chicago.

Name	Hangzhou Bay Bridge
Location	Hangzhou Bay, China
Type	Cable stayed bridge
Function	Six-lane road bridge
Pylon height	89m (292ft)
Deck height	62m (203ft)
Main spans	448 and 318m (1,470 and 1,043ft)
Length	36km (22.3 miles)
Opened	1 May 2008

174

ECONOMIC LANDMARK

At the time of writing the Hangzhou Bay Bridge is the world's longest cross-sea bridge linking the financial hub of Shanghai to the city of Ningbo to the south. This enables the port at Ningbo to compete with its counterpart Shanghai for handling sea freight. As a result of the bridge, the road journey from Ningbo to Shanghai has been shortened by 120km (74.6 miles) and travelling time between the two cities has been reduced from four to two hours. Many businesses are setting up in Hangzhou Bay New Zone, the starting point of the bridge in Ningbo, taking advantage of the newly convenient location and lower costs compared with the Shanghai area. The bridge was financed by a public-private sector infrastructure project, with private investors funding almost 30 per cent of the costs. Construction started in 2003 and finished ahead of schedule in 2007, though the bridge was not opened to the public until May 2008. Capital costs are expected to be recovered through tolls during its first 15 years of service.

WITHSTANDING NATURE

Preparation for the bridge started as early as 1994. The challenge was complex: as the world's longest cross-sea bridge it must withstand summer typhoons sweeping in

Right With six lanes, the Hangzhou Bay Bridge is designed as a major artery to help bring Ningbo and northern Zhejiang into the Greater Shanghai economic area.

BRIDGES OF THE WORLD

HANGZHOU BAY BRIDGE

from the Pacific as well as the phenomenal tides which make Hangzhou Bay a major tourist attraction. Working near the south shore, with fast tides and alternating wet and dry conditions, presented particular technical problems for the construction company as sections of the bridge had to be winched into position over expanses of quicksand-like mudflats.

THE SILVER DRAGON
The wave of the world's largest tidal bore, known as the Silver Dragon, forms at the mouth of the Qiantang River where it joins the Hangzhou Bay. The surging wall of water caused by the movement of the tide along

the narrower river channel, can be up to 9m (29.5ft) high, travelling at up to 40kmph (24.9mph). A cable-stayed design, capable of resisting earthquakes measuring up to 7 on the Richter scale, was selected to withstand these difficult conditions. The S-shaped plan of the bridge is intended not to disturb the Silver Dragon. A further challenge faced by the project was the discovery of natural gas in a shallow layer along the bridge line: this had to be released before the piles were driven, to prevent any collapsing of the ground or ignition of released gas.

The sheer length of the bridge has meant that flashing lights of different colours have

been installed along the bridge to help to prevent driver drowsiness.

A SITE FOR TOURISM
Future developments for the project include a sightseeing platform planned for the middle of the span, including hotels, restaurants and a viewing tower. It is expected that this will be built on piers to avoid disrupting the tide, and may prove to be a popular tourist destination. Indeed, when the bridge first opened to traffic in May 2008, hundreds of drivers were fined for driving too slowly or illegal parking on the bridge while they enjoyed the view and took photographs.

THE DONGHAI BRIDGE
Also serving Shanghai, the Donghai Bridge was completed in 2005 and, at 32.5km (20.2 miles), briefly held the record for the world's longest cross-sea bridge until the Hangzhou Bay Bridge took the title. Connecting the city with the island deep-water port of Yangshan, construction took just two and a half years. Much of the bridge is a low-level viaduct but cable-stayed spans, the largest of which is 420m

(1,378ft) wide, allow large ships to pass. As well as serving Yangshan, the bridge is intended as a future tourist gateway for visitors to other islands in the East China Sea, and will provide a platform for wind turbines.

Below Construction of one of the cable-stayed deck sections of the Donghai Bridge which today carries 6 lanes of traffic to and from Shanghai.

176

Right Six hundred experts spent nine years designing the Hangzhou Bay Bridge – nearly twice as long as the construction process. The bridge opened on 1 May 2008, just under five years after work began.

LUGOU BRIDGE

NEAR BEIJING / **CHINA**

Famous in China as the scene of the trigger point for its war with Japan (1937–1945) this bridge is best known in Europe for being described in the 13th century by Venetian traveller and explorer Marco Polo (1254–1324), who spent 16 years in China. Indeed, it is now also known as the Marco Polo Bridge.

A BRIDGE WITH 'FEW EQUALS'

During his 16 years in China, from 1278-1292, Marco Polo worked for Kublai Khan and later served as Governor of Yangzhou. His subsequent book about his travels enthralled the educated elite of medieval Europe and resulted in a greater awareness of Chinese culture. In his diaries he writes: 'over this river there is a very fine stone bridge, so fine indeed, that it has very few equals in the world'. His account of the Lugou Bridge would have impressed Europeans, whose best examples of stone bridges were mostly survivals from the Roman period. The revival of stone arch

bridge-building techniques in Europe did not come until the late 12th century – the original bridge at Avignon (see page 72) was an almost exact contemporary with the Lugou Bridge.

LIONS WITHIN LIONS

The Lugou Bridge that Marco Polo would have seen, built in 1192, would have been less than a century old at the time. It was destroyed by floods in the 17th century and rebuilt under Emperor Kangxi in 1698. The bridge is built in granite with a larger central arch and ten smaller arches and adorned with 250 marble balustrades

Right The stone lions that stand upon the pillars of the bridge each have more lions carved upon their heads, backs, undersides and on their paws. Despite investigations into the total number, no official number has yet been agreed.

topped by stone lions. Triangular iron pillars were added to the piers to help to prevent damage by flood and ice.

It is said to be impossible to count the Lugou Bridge lions accurately. Smaller lion sculptures are semi-concealed and form part of the larger ones, and accounts of their number vary by a dozen or more. There are nearly 500 lions now, and originally there were said to be 627: they have been added over the centuries, and a few survive from the original pre-1698 bridge. Reclining stone elephants and other carved animals are also found at each end of the bridge, alongside ornamental columns and inscribed marble plaques, one recording the story of its rebuilding by Emperor Kangxi of the Qing Dynasty in 1698, and the other with calligraphy by his grandson Emperor Qianlong, reading 'Lugou Xiaoyue' (Moon over Lugou at daybreak).

VIEWS OF THE MOON

Marco Polo was not the first visitor to appreciate the bridge. Shortly after it was first built in 1192, it appeared in a list of 'eight scenic spots of Yanjing (Beijing)' under

this title, and it was particularly famous for its views of the moon during the mid-autumn festival.

The Yongding River was notorious for its fast and strong currents. Emperor Kangxi had its name changed to Yongding ('eternal stability') from Wuding ('lacking stability') in an attempt to regulate its flow, but it was not until the construction of a reservoir upstream in 1949 that the river was brought fully under control. The Lugou bridge now spans little more than a grassy meadow.

TRIGGER POINT

In July 1937, the bridge was the scene of a dramatic incident that sparked off the war between Japan and China. Japanese forces at its western end shelled the town of Wanping on the other side and marched across the bridge accompanied by tanks. Their subsequent agreement to withdraw proved short-lived, and they advanced across again to take control of Beijing six weeks later. It says much for the quality of the Lugou Bridge's construction that it stood up to the weight of a mechanised army on the move.

Name	Lugou Bridge
Location	Near Beijing, China
Crosses	Yongding River
Type	Arch bridge
Function	road bridge
Main span	21.6m (71ft)
Length	260m (853ft)
Opened	1192, rebuilt 1698

Left The pavilion at the head of the Lugou Bridge is home to a white marble stele bearing the inscription of 'Logouxioayue', or 'The Moon over Logou Bridge at Dawn', in the handwriting of Emperor Qianlong, the grandson of Kangxi, who ordered the reconstruction of the bridge.

PRECIOUS BELT BRIDGE

Also known as Baodai, this bridge near Suzhou, some 80km (50 miles) west of Shanghai, is the longest multi-arched ancient bridge surviving in China. It is near the southern end of China's Grand Canal, which has stretched the 1,770km (1,100 miles) from Beijing to Hangzhou since the 7th century AD. Work on the bridge began in AD816, when it was recorded that local governor Wang Zhongshu generously sold his precious jade belt to help to finance construction, thus giving the bridge its name. The present structure dates from the last rebuilding in 1446 and consists of 53 granite arches with a total length of 317m (1,040ft). The three central arches are enlarged to give a higher clearance of 7.5m (25ft) and allow larger boats to pass.

Precious Belt Bridge has featured in many poems inspired by the local landscape of lakes, rivers, fields and mountains, for example, these lines from philosopher Lu Shiyi (1611-1672):

The water of Dan-tai Lake is shiny green,
The Precious Belt Bridge floats like a silk ribbon.
If possible, I would plant groves of peaches,
And then enjoy every spring amid the flowers.

HOWRAH BRIDGE

KOLKATA / **INDIA**

Also known as the Rabindra Setu Bridge, the Howrah Bridge is a legacy of British rule in India. One of the busiest bridges in the world, it is regarded as the lifeline of the city and has become an iconic structure of India.

A PEOPLE'S BRIDGE

Unusually for a great cantilever bridge, it is a vital link for pedestrians as well as vehicles. Around four million crossings on foot and around 150,000 vehicle crossings are made each day between Howrah, home to one of the world's largest railway terminals, and Kolkata itself.

The new Howrah Bridge replaced Kolkata's Floating Pontoon Bridge of 1874. Designed by Sir Bradford Leslie and intended only to last a third as long as it eventually did, the Pontoon Bridge helped the new port of Kolkata to develop by connecting it to the industrial satellite of Howrah. It had a 60-metre (197ft) opening section to allow shipping through, and hinged spans connecting to the shore to allow the bridge to float up and down with the tides. However, the steepness of their slope at high tide meant that bullock carts could not pass, and this caused immense congestion at each end as traffic increased. There were also concerns that the bridge was causing the harbour to silt up.

WAR AND CONGESTION

Construction of the new bridge commenced in 1937, with design and building by British engineering firms using mostly Indian steel and labour. The two 40,000-tonne piers supporting the towers were, unusually, built on each shore rather than in the water; when one suddenly subsided by half a metre (1.6ft) during construction the shock is claimed to have caused a nearby Hindu temple to fall down.

When it opened to traffic in February 1943, Howrah Bridge immediately facilitated the Allied war effort, giving troops better access to the industrial suburb of Howrah and the road to the front in Burma. After the war its traffic soon exceeded the busiest bridge in London, London Bridge, by about 20 per cent. A survey in May 1946 observed crossings by 27,400 vehicles, 121,100 pedestrians and 2,997 cattle. Today there is concern about massively increased congestion, though downstream the Second Hooghly Bridge (1993) has helped congestion.

Howrah Bridge was repainted and illuminated as part of its 60th anniversary celebrations; its trademark aluminium-coloured paintwork is now lit up every night in gold and magenta.

Name	Howrah Bridge
Location	Kolkata, India
Crosses	Hooghly River
Type	Cantilever bridge
Function	Road and pedestrian bridge (originally also carried trams)
Span	458m (1,501ft)
Length	705m (2,313ft)
Height	82m (269ft)
Clearance	8.8m (29ft)
Opened	February 1943
Design	Rendel Palmer & Tritton

FLOATING BRIDGES

Pontoon or floating bridges have a deck supported by boat- or barge-like floating supports, rather than anchored piers. Temporary pontoon bridges, originally using real ships positioned side by side, are recorded in ancient Chinese acounts as early as the 11th century BC. A Greek engineer, Mandrocles of Samos, constructed a pontoon bridge across the Bosporus between Europe and Asia for the army of Darius I the Great of Persia (522BC–486BC). Even now they are important in warfare – the US army constructed one 620 metres long across the River Sava between Croatia and Bosnia in 1995, and used a modern version, the 'Assault Float Ribbon Bridge', in the Gulf War of 2003.

Pontoon bridges are not confined to the ancient and military worlds. Lake Washington, near Seattle, US, is spanned by a number of floating bridges, chosen as the most practical option for a lake that averages 43 metres deep without strong currents or tides. As Kolkata was replacing the first Howrah pontoon bridge, an innovative one in concrete was being unveiled to general amazement in the US. One Homer H. Hadley, who had worked on concrete ships and barges as a substitute for steel ones during the First World War, originally proposed a floating bridge on Lake Washington in 1920. The first one, the 2,020-metre (6,627-foot) long Murrow Bridge, opened to traffic in 1940. Many people had not believed it would float, and marvelled that it was larger than the largest ocean liner of its day. However, it sank dramatically in 1990, with each connected pontoon filling with water, upending in turn and descending into the water. It has been rebuilt to a similar design with modern safety features.

Left Withstanding the famously stormy weather of the region, the 26,000 million tons of steel in the Howrah Bridge can expand by as much as a metre on a hot summer's day.

SI-O-SE POL

ESFAHAN / **IRAN**

In the midst of one of Iran's great historic cities, this remarkable
17th-century structure was not built solely as a means of crossing
from one side of the Zaandeh River to the other, but also as a
contemplative retreat from the harsh desert heat.

PART OF A GRAND PLAN

Si-o-se Pol – meaning the 'bridge of 33
arches' – was originally named Allahverdi
Khan Bridge, after its designer, who was the
Army Commander-in-Chief to Shah Abbas I
of the Safavid Dynasty of Persia (now Iran).
In 1598, the Shah had selected Esfahan, in
the centre of the country, as his new capital
and the bridge was just one element in a
grand scheme of highways, palaces, mosques
and villas, all in a lush garden setting. It
linked the main boulevard in Esfahan to the
Armenian quarter of New Jolfa.

A PUBLIC ORNAMENT

The 33 pointed arches, 5.6m (18.4ft) across,
are on the lower level, which has a broad
roadway, with the piers standing on
exceptionally wide bases. The upper deck
has two arches above each lower one, and
its deck is divided into three strips. In the
centre is a broad aisle intended as a passage

for animals and carts, while the sides were
built as for pedestrians to take time in the
shade and to enjoy the river views from the
arcaded galleries. These galleries, decorated
with paintings, were also intended to serve
as rooms for fatigued travellers to rest in.
The idea of a bridge as both an ornament
and a public space was very much in
keeping with the style of town planning
and architecture introduced during by the
rulers of the Safavid Dynasty (1501-1722),
with geometric street plans and open spaces
cooled by planting and water features.

CONSTRUCTION FORESIGHT

The structure is made of sand, brick and
locally made concrete, decorated with
tiles, with a tea house built on one side.
The bridge no longer takes traffic, but is
still very much used as a popular meeting
place for people from the city. In 2006,
the construction of the Esfahan metro

underground railway system was reported
to be threatening the bridge and other
Safavid monuments through the leakage
of groundwater, despite the fact that
the original bridge builders understood
potential problems with water and
sealed the foundations as a result.

Name	Si-o-se Pol
Location	Esfahan, Iran
Crosses	Zaandeh River
Type	Double-deck multi-arch bridge
Function	Road bridge
Length	298m (977ft)
Opened	1602
Design	Allahverdi Khan

Right The bridge at Si-o-se Pol was built under the
Safavid Dynasty which favoured strong geometrical
designs that gave order to urban environments.

KHAJU BRIDGE (PUL-KHAJU)

Another of the celebrated bridges in Esfahan, this post-dates the Si-o-se Pol by half a century. It
was built around 1650 by Shah Abbas II on the foundations of an older bridge. It is slightly smaller
than Si-o-se Pol, with 23 arches and a length of 105m (345ft), but displays some similar concepts
in a refined form. It has two decks, with the upper one divided between a carriageway and two
side aisles for pedestrians. The niches overlooking the river are spacious, creating outdoor rooms,
and there are six multi-sided pavilions known as 'Princes' Parlours' used as vantage points.

  Beneath is a roadway wide enough for five lanes of traffic, with vaulted bays, piers and arches.
On its western side, the water pours over steps, which doubled as a gathering ground for local
people. The bridge also functions as a weir, and was also used as a retreat from the heat.

Right The vaults of the Khaju Bridge. The structure also functions as a weir; a stone dam impounds the river to
create a reservoir, originally to provide an ornamental setting for the palaces and pavilions either side of the river.

AKASHI-KAIKYO BRIDGE

KOBE / **JAPAN**

The technology of suspension bridge-building took a new leap forward with this record-breaking bridge, also known as the Pearl Bridge. It forms part of the Honshu-Shikoku Bridge Project which has joined up Japan's two largest islands by means of three routes and 16 links over the 100-metre (328-foot) deep Seto Inland Sea.

REPLACING THE FERRY

Together with the Onarutu Bridge, the three-span Akashi-Kaikyo Bridge forms a link from the city of Kobe to Shikoku via Awaji Island, and takes six lanes of road traffic. There has been considerable political pressure to erect a bridge since two ferries collided in 1955, killing 168 people (most of them children). The challenge faced by architects was to design a central span of nearly 2km (1.2 miles) that could give substantial clearance for vessels in the Akashi Strait, one of the world's busiest shipping lanes. It also needed to withstand typhoon winds of up to 290kph and earthquakes measuring up to 8.5 on the Richter scale. Construction finally began in 1988 and took an estimated two million man-days over ten years, with 1.4 million cubic metres of concrete and enough steel cable to circle the world seven times.

RECORD BREAKER

The completed structure overtook the previous record-holder, the Humber Bridge (see page 146), to achieve the longest suspension bridge span in the world. At four times the length of Brooklyn Bridge and with the world's tallest bridge towers, it has been hailed by many critics as Japan's greatest engineering feat to date. To cope with all that the elements can hurl at it, the bridge is supported with a truss – a complex of triangular braces – that give the bridge rigidity while avoiding a solid structure that would create too much wind resistance. The bridge is also designed to cope with expansion through heating of up to 2m (6.6ft) during any one day.

PRECISION BUILDING

The 60-metre (197-foot) high circular foundations of the towers were made by building moulds in a dry dock. These were then towed out by tugs and positioned, before being filled with 50 million litres of sea water, and then with a special concrete that could be mixed with sea water. The towers comprise 90 sections each, designed to flex in storm winds. Each is installed with 20 specially tuned mass dampers, a system of devices that move weights around to counteract vertical movements caused by the wind. Some 750,000 bolts were used in the construction of the towers. To achieve precision building, the surface of each section was ground to a smooth finish.

Name	Akashi-Kaikyo Bridge
Location	Connects Kobe with Awaji Island
Type	Suspension bridge
Function	Road bridge
Main span	1,991m (6,532ft)
Total length	3,800m (12,467ft)
Pylon height	283m (928ft)
Crosses	Seto Inland Sea
Completed	1998
Architects	Honshu-Shikoku Bridge Authority

Right and previous page A total of 1,737 lights illuminate the Akashi-Kaikyo Bridge, with more than a thousand lighting the main cables alone. Different patterns of light on the bridge are used to mark holidays, festivities and memorial days.

RAINBOW BRIDGE, TOKYO

Completed in 1993, this suspension bridge across Tokyo Harbour and has become a symbol of the regeneration of the Odaiba area of the bayside, and a popular place for Tokyoites and visitors to gather and enjoy views of Tokyo Tower and on clear days the distant peak of Mount Fuji. Its two decks comprise an upper stage carrying an expressway and a lower stage with a road, a walkway and an unmanned express train, the Yurikamome New Transit. The total length is 918m (3,012ft), with 570m (1,870ft) extending between the two white towers. Solar energy powers the ornamental red, white and green lights.

Below Taking just over six years to build, the Tatara Bridge was surpassed only in 2008 as the world's longest cable-stayed bridge, when the Sutong Bridge across the Yangtze River in China opened.

TATARA BRIDGE

Another part of the Honshu-Shikoku Bridge Project and on the road route which also crosses the Kurushima-Kaikyo Bridge, the Tatara Bridge was initially conceived in 1973 as a suspension bridge, which would have required extensive excavation for an anchorage. Sixteen years later, the plan was changed to create what became the longest steel-concrete hybrid type cable-stayed bridge in the world on its completion in 1999. The pre-stressed concrete box girders on the ends of the side spans were an innovation that allowed the span to be increased further than if the bridge was a cable-stayed structure alone. It has a main span 890m (2,919ft) of a total length of 1,480m (4,856ft), and a clearance of 26m (85ft), with its two towers, each shaped like an inverted Y, rising to 200m (656ft). The fan shape of the cables has been likened to a white bird spreading its wings. The bridge carries four lanes of traffic and lanes for bicycles, motor bikes and pedestrians.

KINTAI BRIDGE

IWAKUNI / JAPAN

One of a trio of Japan's best-known historic bridges, the 'Bridge of the Brocade Sash' (as it is also known) is held by the Japanese in special affection for its shapely beauty, and has been depicted by many Japanese artists. Illuminated at night and crossing a clear-watered river, it is much-frequented during cherry blossom time in spring.

A STRUCTURE OF RENEWAL

Whether this is an original structure is open to debate, as nothing remains of what was first erected here in 1673 by the feudal lord Hirohoshi Kikkawa, of the nearby castle. However, according to Japanese literature, it was intended that reconstruction of the superstructure would occur every decade. However, practically, because of deterioration or damage, many repairs and replications were completed over the bridge's lifetime. This echoes a widely observed Japanese spiritual need to keep a structure from decaying: otherwise it threatens the continuity that is essential for the wellbeing of mankind. Indeed, many Japanese wooden monuments such as castles, shrines and temples are regularly renewed, in a country prone to typhoons, earthquakes and high levels of humidity.

AN IMPROVED DESIGN

Being capable of surviving floods was key to the bridge's design, and it was frequently used as an escape route in times when the flood levels were too high for local people to be ferried across. After earlier spans had been washed away, it emerged that that driftwood in the river was building up pressure on piers and led to their eventual collapse. An improved design saw the creation of four stone-walled islets evenly spaced in the shallow river, and experiments were made with various designs and test structures before final completion in 1673. It washed away the following year, but then the footings of the piers were improved and the bridge lasted 276 years until a typhoon in 1950. The complete rebuilding in 1953 used chemically treated timbers, and the stone piers were reinforced with concrete cores; it has had two partial reconstructions since 2001.

INSPIRATION

With its steep walkway following the curve arches, the design is thought to have been inspired by similar bridges in China. It may have come from stories told by a Ming Dynasty Chinese priest who settled in Japan and spread the message about the stone arched bridge of his native country – or from an existing Japanese span such as Saruhashi Bridge in Otuki.

Right Along with the nearby Iwakuni Castle, the Kintai Bridge has long made the local town of Iwakuni a draw for visitors from Japan and abroad.

Name	Kintai Bridge
Location	Iwakuni, Japan
Crosses	Nishiki River
Type	Five-arched timber bridge
Total span	196m (642ft)
Deck width	5m (16ft)
Completed	1673

Left and Right The Kintai Bridge is celebrated by a local festival each April, held at the nearby Kikko Park. The festival includes a parade across the bridge featuring local people dressed in historic samurai costumes who re-enact ancient practices.

EXOTIC BRIDGES AS ORNAMENTS

The Western fashion for Japanese style partly derived from the Japanese prints that appeared in the late 19th century after Japan opened itself to the Western world, having been a closed society until 1868. Japanese-inspired gardens were developed, and with them arched wooden footbridges.

The taste for installing exotic bridges in Western gardens dates from the 19th century. The first Japanese garden in the United States was at Golden Gate Park, a short distance south of Golden Gate Bridge (see page 232). This was the site of the Japanese Village at the 1894 California Midwinter International Exposition which includes surviving landscape features such as a pagoda and teahouse, and the Taiko-Bashi Drum Bridge, made by Shinshichi Nakatani, a Japanese master shrine builder.

One of the most enduring images of a Japanese-style bridge is that at Giverny, France, in the garden of the house once owned by the Impressionist painter Claude Monet. Here he created a water garden, inspired by Japanese prints he had seen, and had a small timber arched bridge built in Japanese style. The walkway followed the same curve as the arch, and the wooden railings were painted green rather than the traditional Japanese vermillion. This became the subject of a series of some of his best-known paintings.

A fanciful Chinese bridge appears on the much-produced willow pattern design made popular from the late 18th century by the English ceramicist Thomas Minton. The Chinese-style bridge also occurs here and there in country estates, such as at Island Hall in Godmanchester, Cambridgeshire, where the 'Chinese Bridge' dates from 1827, though it was later rebuilt. Painshill Park, in Surrey, was a creation of the early 18th century by Charles Hamilton who like many others of the period

created a landscaped park dotted with various Italianate fancies inspired by his Grand Tour of Europe, and added a Chinese bridge for good measure. Elsewhere the aristocratic stately homes of England often favoured classical architecture in park bridge design during that period. Stowe Landscape Garden has a Chinese teahouse, but the bridge of 1742 is inspired by the Italian Renaissance architect Palladio, and copied from an earlier one at Wilton House near Salisbury. Stowe's Palladian Bridge was adapted for use by carriages, so that it was possible to ride over it while making a tour of the grounds.

Below The iconic Japanese bridge that is the centrepiece for the water garden at Monet's house at Giverny was originally built by a local craftsman, and covered with wisterias planted by the artist himself.

AUSTRALASIA

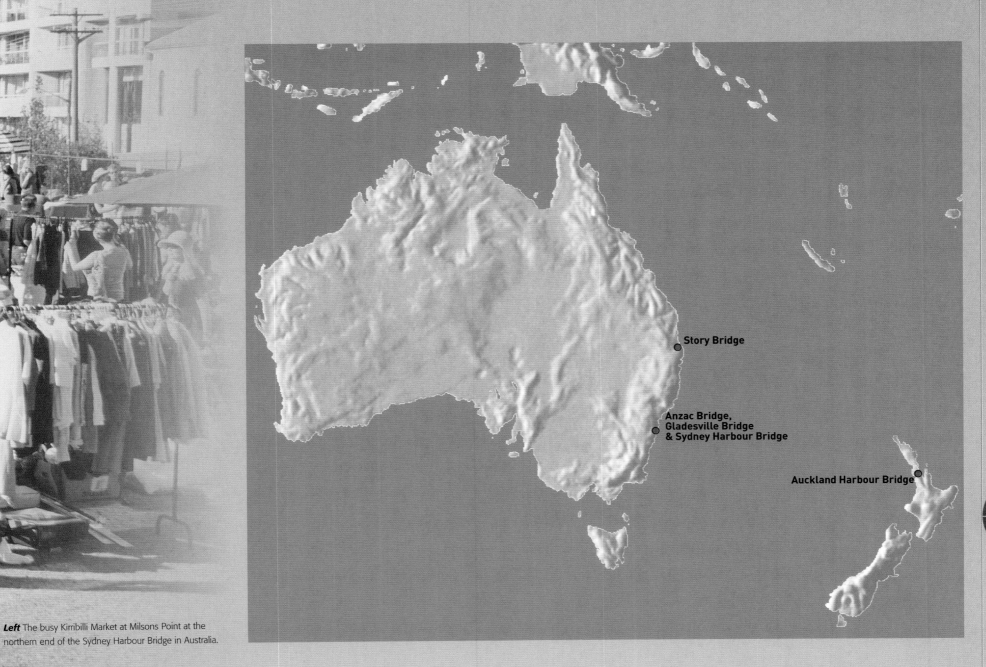

Story Bridge

Anzac Bridge,
Gladesville Bridge
& Sydney Harbour Bridge

Auckland Harbour Bridge

Left The busy Kirribilli Market at Milsons Point at the northern end of the Sydney Harbour Bridge in Australia.

STORY BRIDGE

BRISBANE / **AUSTRALIA**

Like the Sydney Harbour Bridge, Brisbane's Story Bridge
seized the imagination of a city during the Great Depression
and provided respite from the news of the Second World War.
It is still regarded with great affection today.

SYMBOL OF PROGRESS

As capital of the State of Queensland and
Australia's third-largest city, Brisbane was
already suffering road-traffic congestion in
the city centre by the 1920s, when a series
of new bridges over the Brisbane River was
proposed. Story Bridge was the second of
these, with construction beginning in 1935
as part of a public works programme to
relieve local unemployment. During this
era of worldwide economic difficulties and
political unrest, new bridges came to be
seen as far more than simply transport
projects. Their construction could be a
symbol of hope and progress and a focus
for a city's pride. In addition, despite the
depression, the developing automobile
traffic of the US and Australia held out the
promise of ever-increasing toll revenue from
new road bridges, an incentive to far-sighted
authorities to provide the funds which
were needed for bridge construction. The
economic model of funding bridge-building
from tolls was an ancient one, but had come
to look feasible again by the 1930s.

THE SYDNEY CONNECTION

Dr John Bradfield (1847–1943), designer of
the Story Bridge, had been chief engineer
for the Sydney Harbour Bridge and had
proposed an underground railway scheme
for Sydney as early as 1915. He also

Right One of the great motivations behind the bridge was to stimulate the economy during the Depression. Almost all
the construction materials were Australian, and 89 per cent of the total cost was spent within the state of Queensland.

STORY BRIDGE

designed dams, and drew up an ambitious plan, never fulfilled, to irrigate the western side of Australia's Great Dividing Range by diverting some of Queensland's rivers. He moved on from the Sydney Harbour Bridge to start work on the Story Bridge in 1934, and construction began the following year. It was a source of pride to Queensland that nearly 90 per cent of the bridge's cost of over $3 million Australian was spent within the State, and that more than 400 people secured work on the bridge during its six years of construction.

HOPE AND CONTROVERSY

The opening ceremony in July 1940 provided Brisbane with a respite from news of the Second World War and was celebrated with many dignitaries in attendance. However, church leaders left early in protest that no blessing of the bridge had been carried out and that the Archbishop had been left sitting in the sun. The bridge was named after John Douglas Story (1869–1966), a prominent former Queensland public official. More than 600,000 pedestrians crossed on the first day of operation and the toll booths were

overwhelmed by as many as 40 cars arriving every minute.

A POSITIVE FUTURE

The bridge was regarded as a symbol of the achievements of the people of Queensland and of hope for the future after the war. The Premier of Queensland saw the structure as 'a monument to the vision, enterprise and engineering prowess of our own people' and John Bradfield commented that '...under the stimulus of the bridge, Queensland would be in a better position to go ahead with its own

nation building after the war'. The bridge featured in marketing campaigns promoting Queensland and Brisbane as progressive, industrial economies.

The Story Bridge is now lit at night, and is a central feature in Brisbane's annual Riverfire festival. Bridge climbing tours were launched in 2005 and were an instant success, with Story Bridge's two and a half hour experience joining the Sydney and Auckland Harbour bridges as one of the only three licensed bridge climbs in the world.

AUCKLAND HARBOUR BRIDGE

This 1,021-metre (3,346-ft) long box truss bridge carries eight lanes of traffic between Auckland and North Shore City, New Zealand. Opened in 1959, its original four lanes rapidly proved inadequate for the needs of the developing suburbs of North Shore, and in 1969 special box girder deck extensions were added on each side to double its capacity. Manufactured by a Japanese firm, these were nicknamed the 'Nippon clip-ons' by the Aucklanders. With a refurbishment programme under way, there is now public pressure to add further clip-ons to provide a walking and cycling crossing – at present the only way to get on the bridge without a vehicle is to take part in a bridge climb or bungee jump.

The Auckland bridge climb experience was developed in 2001 by two local entrepreneurs, one of whom went on to set up the Story Bridge Climb in Brisbane. It followed on from the world's first bridge climb, on Sydney Harbour Bridge, opened in 1998. Vertiginous but safe, these tours have already been taken by several million people. More intrepid thrill-seekers can now enjoy the Auckland Harbour Bridge Bungee and leap 40m (131ft) from a special 'jump pod' installed under the road deck.

Below The Auckland Bridge rises 43m (172ft) above the high water, meaning that ships can access deep water ports such as that at the nearby Chelsea Sugar Refinery.

Name	Story Bridge
Location	Brisbane
Crosses	Brisbane River
Type	Cantilever bridge
Function	Road and pedestrian/ cycle bridge
Main span	282m (924ft)
Length	1,375m (4,511ft)
Clearance	30.4m (100ft)
Opened	6 July 1940
Design	John Bradfield

GLADESVILLE BRIDGE

SYDNEY / AUSTRALIA

One of a notable trio of engineering triumphs in the watery expanses of Sydney Harbour, the Gladesville Bridge was a pioneering use of concrete and at the time the longest single span concrete arch ever constructed. It stands virtually equidistant on the time line between the Sydney Harbour Bridge (1932) and the Anzac Bridge (1995).

GLADESVILLE BRIDGE

THE OLD GLADESVILLE BRIDGE

At a time when the Department for Main Roads (DMR) were aiming to propel Sydney into the road traffic age, the old Gladesville Bridge was barely adequate. Completed in 1881, it carried just two lanes of traffic which was shared with trams and incorporated a swing bridge that was barely wide enough to let coal boats pass through. It also tended to get jammed as the metal expanded in the heat, and water had to be sprayed on it to move it back into the closed position and let traffic across; even then, the tram lines were often out of alignment.

CONCRETE SOLUTION

The London firm Maunsell & Partners was commissioned to build a new span with an exceptionally high clearance to allow for tankers and other large vessels. The first scheme was for a classical steel truss

cantilever structure. However, the then recent development of pre-stressed concrete technology was seen as the better solution, and the topography of the area was ideal for the high approaches that were required. The bridge was built on sandstone foundations and consisted of four arched ribs, built with six traffic lanes and two walkways either side. It was opened in 1964 and was widened to seven lanes in 1982.

PIONEERING TECHNIQUES

The designer of the bridge used an idea pioneered by bridge architect Eugène Freyssinet to remove falsework from the arch. It would have been too dangerous and difficult to employ the traditional method of inserting wedges into the temporary supporting falsework then removing them at the end of the process to free the structure from the arch itself. So the hollow blocks

of each rib were transported by barge, lifted up and transferred by trolley onto the steel falsework and lowered down either side. Once the blocks were in place, gaskets within the blocks were inflated with a hydraulic fluid – this had the effect of raising the arch away from the formwork and enabling it to become self-supporting.

The falsework was then removed and prepared for the next rib of the arch. All the ribs were then joined with cables, stressed together and concreted. The ribs also had cables attached to them, but they appear to have been superfluous; in the words of one construction worker 'they were a bit of a joke…I thought they were just a face saver and didn't think they did much good. …they made people feel better.' A special concrete testing laboratory was set up on the site to test load capabilities and to manage

the quality of the concrete; the high target strength was unprecedented.

PERSEVERANCE

The work took six years to complete; it was partially dogged by union strikes, and by the financial disarray of the main contractor, who went into receivership. But the workmen knew this project was something special. Soon after the bridge's opening, the trade press journal *Concrete Quarterly* stated 'what the four-minute mile was to runners…the 305-metre (1,001-foot) span has long been to the designers of concrete bridges'. The steep gradient has been blamed for numerous traffic accidents on the bridge, but it has generally been a success, and the structure has proved well up to the task, requiring minimal maintenance. In 1990 the National Trust of Australia listed the bridge as a heritage site.

Name	Gladesville Bridge
Location	Sydney
Crosses	Parramatta River
Type	Reinforced concrete arch
Function	Freeway bridge
Main span	305m (1,001ft)
Length	488m (1,601ft)
Clearance	40.7m (134ft)
Opened	1964
Design	Maunsell & Partners

Left The Gladesville Bridge, the world's largest single span concrete arch, was built with an extremely high clearance in anticipation of the greater size of future sea-going vessels.

Right The Gladesville Bridge (foreground) spans the Paramatta River whilst the Sydney Harbour Bridge to the east (top left of image) carries traffic between the CBD and the North Shore of Sydney.

SYDNEY HARBOUR BRIDGE

SYDNEY / **AUSTRALIA**

The world's widest long-span bridge, this immense single-arch steel construction is Sydney's defining landmark, alongside the nearby Opera House, and one of the most enduring symbols of Australia. It was inspired by New York City's Hell Gate and, when completed in 1932, was widely regarded as the ultimate in modern bridge design.

FIRST PROPOSALS

The creation of a bridge over the tidal waters of Sydney Harbour was drawn out in the extreme. It was first suggested in 1815 by Francis Greenway, a convict, and later that century other plans were proposed. Building a masonry, wood or cast-iron bridge was judged too costly and difficult to achieve, but with the advent of prefabricated steel and reinforced concrete the scheme at last became a reality. In 1890 a royal commission sought a solution to reducing ferry traffic; it took another 21 years before John Bradfield was appointed chief engineer for the project. He submitted his design for a single-arch bridge in 1916, but with the

intervention of the First World War, work did not start until 1922.

Bradfield opted for a two-hinged arch design as one strong and durable enough for the task. The arch bears the weight of the deck, while the hinges at each end support the bridge's full weight and spread the load to the foundations, while allowing the steel to expand and contract with changes in temperature.

THE IRON LUNG

The contract for construction was awarded to Dorman Long and Co. of Middlesbrough, England (also responsible for the Tyne Bridge in Newcastle upon Tyne), with Ralph Freeman as consulting engineer. In these depression-hit years the project needed to benefit the Australian economy, so it was stipulated wherever possible that materials had to be sourced from New South Wales and that local people would be employed. In the event 79 per cent of the steel was manufactured in Middlesbrough, and some specialist workers were imported, but the building of the bridge certainly did boost

the national economy – it was named the Iron Lung as it took on some 1,400 Depression-era workers. However, after its completion, many faced a long period without employment.

Also nicknamed the 'coat hanger', the bridge carries the busy six-lane Bradfield Highway, two railway lines that form part of the city underground system, a cycle way and a footway and until 1958 it was also used by trams.

THE STRUCTURE

The concrete deck lies on lengthwise-placed beams, or 'trimmers', resting on steel cross beams. The 39,000-tonne single arch rises to 134m (440ft) above mean sea level. Some six million rivets, made at the Park Bridge Ironworks in Lancashire, England, were hand-driven into the whole structure, the painting of which requires 80,000 litres to coat an area equivalent to 60 football pitches. The four piers are decorative rather than functional, and are finished with granite quarried at Moruya on the coast of New South Wales, where a temporary

Name	Sydney Harbour Bridge
Location	Sydney Harbour/Port Jackson
Crosses	Sydney Harbour
Type	Single arch bridge
Function	Road and rail bridge
Span	503m (1,650ft)
Length	1,149m (3,770ft)
Clearance	52.4m (172ft) at low tide
Opened	19 March 1932
Design	John Bradfield and Ralph Freeman

Right The view from Milson's Point at the north end of the bridge takes in the Sydney skyline and the high-rise office buildings of the central business district.

SYDNEY HARBOUR BRIDGE

Above The southern end under construction in 1929. Two separate teams started on the arch at either end of the bridge with the southern end working a month ahead so that errors could be passed to the northern side.

settlement of Australian, Scottish and Italian stonemasons was set up. Work commenced in 1923, and after the approach spans were erected the main arch was begun in 1928. It was manufactured in two sections at workshops set up at Milsons Point on the North Shore, then towed out on barges and lifted by electrically operated creeper cranes, and joined together in 1930. Anchoring tunnels were dug into the rock to secure the supporting cables.

OPENING AND PROTEST

The official opening day on Saturday 19 March 1932 drew a huge crowd estimated variously at something between 300,000 and a million people. Processions, bands and a pageant boosted the festival atmosphere, which was marred by one Captain Francis De Groot, a right-wing extremist paramilitary of an organization calling itself the New Guard. He charged in

on his horse and, before anyone could stop him, prematurely sliced the ribbon with his sword and declared 'In the name of the loyal and decent citizens of NSW, I declare this Bridge open', prior to the official opening by Premier Jack Lang – to the mirth of some and indignation of others. He was fined £5 for his actions, and has been a part of Australian folklore ever since.

ATTRACTION AND ICON

In 1988, the construction costs of the bridge were finally recovered by income from tolls, and that same year the public was first allowed to climb along catwalks, up ladders to the very top of the bridge – an experience that has become a top tourist attraction. To ease traffic flow across the bridge, the Sydney Harbour Tunnel was completed in 1992. The money generated from bridge and tunnel tolls continues to fund maintenance and repair work.

Right The deck of the bridge carries the six-lane Bradfield Highway, at 2.4km (1.5 miles) the shortest highway in Australia. A further two lanes support the Cahill Expressway in a southerly direction only.

ANZAC BRIDGE

Opened in 1995 as Glebe Island Bridge, this is another striking landmark structure in Sydney, connecting the city centre with the western suburbs. It takes an eight-lane freeway and a very broad pathway shared between pedestrians and cyclists. With its central span of 345m (1,132ft) it is Australia's longest cable-stayed bridge, and among the largest of its kind in the world. The concrete pylons rise to 120m (394ft).

On Remembrance Day in 1998 it was renamed Anzac Bridge in honour of the soldiers of the Australian and New Zealand Army Corps (ANZACs) who served in the First World War. Australian and New Zealand

flags fly from each of the pylons, and at the western end statues of an Australian soldier, or 'Digger' and a New Zealand soldier stand either side of the carriageway. A handful of sand from Gallipoli was placed beneath the foot of the Digger in remembrance of those who died in action at the Gallipoli Battlefield in Turkey.

Below The Anzac Bridge supports the Western Distributor freeway leading away from the Sydney Central Business District. It crosses Johnstons Bay between the Sydney suburbs of Pyrmont and Rozelle.

NORTH AMERICA

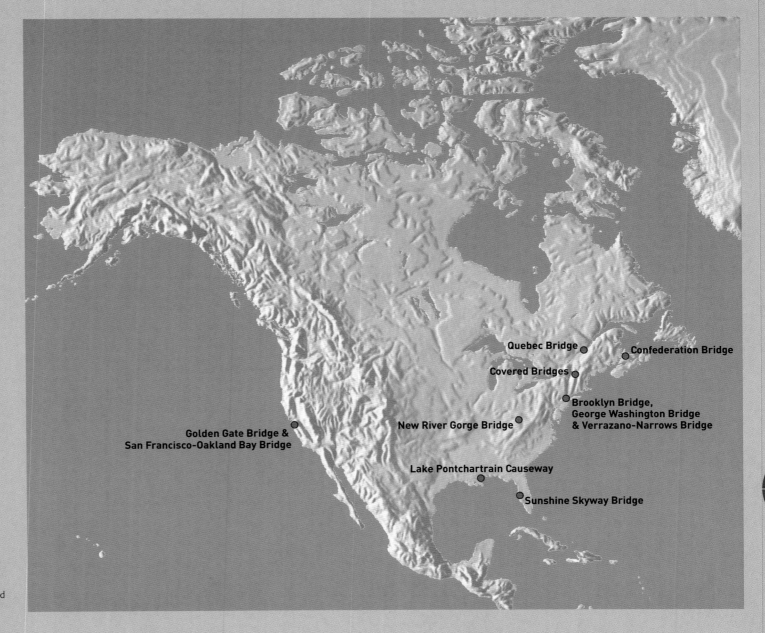

Quebec Bridge

Confederation Bridge

Covered Bridges

Brooklyn Bridge,
George Washington Bridge
& Verrazano-Narrows Bridge

New River Gorge Bridge

Golden Gate Bridge &
San Francisco-Oakland Bay Bridge

Lake Pontchartrain Causeway

Sunshine Skyway Bridge

207

Left The New York City Marathon begins on Staten Island
near the approach to the Verrazano-Narrows Bridge.

CONFEDERATION BRIDGE

PORT BORDEN AND PRINCE EDWARD ISLAND / **CANADA**

The joining of Prince Edward Island to New Brunswick required building the world's longest bridge over ice-covered waters. Something of a tourist attraction in its own right, it has brought new prosperity to the island.

MAKING A CASE

Ever since Prince Edward Island became a province of Canada in 1873, there was talk of a fixed link with the mainland, across the narrowest point of the Northumberland Strait, which is iced up for five months of the year. In the 19th century scheduled steamboats made the crossing, and in winter mariners rowed ice boats and picked their way across icy stretches, conveying passengers and cargo. It was a treacherous way across, and the fixed link question became a Federal election issue. Schemes proposed in the 1950s and 1960s included a causeway across Abegweit Passage, and a tunnel or a bridge across the rest of the Strait. This was rejected on the grounds that it would make navigation difficult, and that closing off part of the Strait would create tidal currents to surge through the gap.

When, in 1988, the islanders voted on the question of a fixed link, intense public debate ensued. Many feared the loss of jobs among ferry workers and the effects on the fishing industry, and there were concerns that a bridge would not be able to stand up to the wind and ice. But most were in favour.

INNOVATION IN ARCHITECTURE

In the event, one the world's longest, continuous, multi-span bridges was begun in 1993 and completed in three and a half years in extremely testing conditions, using particularly durable high-grade concrete and reinforcing steel used for the pre-cast components to provide an estimated lifespan of over 100 years. The structure takes two lanes of traffic and is supported by 62 concrete piers. These were specially cast with cones skirting the bases to act as ice shields, lifting up the ice and causing it to break under its own weight. The main span is taller than the rest to allow shipping through. Because of its 12.9-kilometre (8-mile) length, the bridge is built with a slight curve to encourage better standards of driving and attentiveness than would occur in a straight road.

ECONOMIC EFFECTS

Critics claim the opening of Confederation Bridge has irredeemably eroded the lifestyle of Prince Edward Island. However, it has brought tangible economic benefits. The island's economic activity rose appreciably after the opening of the Confederation

Bridge in 1997, with a notable rise in fortunes for local potato farmers and fishermen, and new retail stores also opened. Tourism increased by 50 per cent a year, although it has since fallen back a little since then.

Name	Confederation Bridge
Location	Port Borden and Prince Edward Island
Crosses	Northumberland Strait
Type	Multi-span concrete box girder bridge
Function	Road bridge
Main span	250m (820ft)
Length	12.9km (8 miles)
Clearance	60m (197ft) (main span)
Opened	1997
Design	J Muller International and Stantec

Right The bridge connects the provinces of Prince Edward Island and New Brunswick, Canada and takes just over 10 minutes to cross by car. It helps bring approximately 900,000 visitors to the island each year.

QUEBEC BRIDGE

QUEBEC / **CANADA**

More than 90 years after its completion and now standing alongside Canada's longest suspension bridge (the Pierre Laporte Bridge) the Quebec Bridge remains the longest cantilever span in the world. However, its construction was dogged by tragedy.

CANTILEVER POSSIBILITIES

The idea to build a bridge to replace the ferry over the St. Lawrence River had been mooted since the 1850s, but it was clear that both the clearance and span would have to be immense for such a structure to allow ocean-going shipping to pass beneath. The solution became a reality with the cantilever principle that had been so successful with the Forth Bridge (see page 138). However, the project was riddled with human error that was to prove fatal on two occasions.

EXTENDING A PRINCIPLE

The celebrated New York engineer Theodore Cooper (1839-1919) had three major civil engineering projects to his name, including the St. Louis Bridge (completed 1874) when he came to tackling this, the biggest and most prestigious assignment of his career. It required a span longer than the Forth Bridge, and would therefore be the longest bridge in the world. Cooper extended the original plan for a central span of 488m (1,601ft), with 183-metre (600-foot) side spans, by a further 61m (200ft). This extra length was created by bringing the piers towards dry land, hence reducing their planned depth and making a saving in the overall cost of the project. The Phoenix Bridge Company were contracted to build the bridge. However, corners were cut on preliminary design and testings, and Cooper's ill health prevented his being on

Right Today, the Quebec Bridge is accompanied across the St. Lawrence River by the Pierre Laporte Bridge (1970). Its more recent neighbour carries six lanes of traffic compared to the three-lane capacity of the older bridge.

the site for long. Worst of all, no one dared challenge the calculations of the great man. Further problems also contributed to the impending disaster at the Quebec Bridge.

There was a crucial delay in getting the working drawings to Cooper, who only received them after work had begun. He noticed the longer span would load the bridge by some eight million pounds more than the earlier estimates – but rather than start again, Cooper trusted that this was

Name	Quebec Bridge
Location	Quebec City
Crosses	St. Lawrence River
Type	Cantilever truss bridge
Function	Road and rail bridge
Main span	549m (1,801ft)
Suspended span	195m (640ft)
Opened	1917

Left The Canadian Pacific ship SS *Melita* sails under the Quebec Bridge close to the point where, only a few years before, the central span crashed into the St. Lawrence as it was being lifted into position.

within safe tolerances, so keen was he to erect the world's largest structure of its kind. The Prince of Wales (later King George V) was due to open the bridge in 1908, and any delay in construction would have caused major problems for what should have been Cooper's greatest triumph.

PRELUDE TO DISASTER
On 15 June 1907, an engineer noticed a misalignment of two girders. Cooper opined that it was 'not serious'; a report two months later said that the girders appeared bent and the alignment was more out of true.

By 27 August, site engineer Norman McLure noted that the girders had moved a 'couple of inches' over the weekend and were even more obviously bent. He went to New York to speak with Cooper in person: telephoning was apparently not an option because Cooper had a party line and the potentially devastating news could fall on the wrong ears. But there was confusion about orders to stop work, construction continued unsupervised, and the weight of the steel sections put too much stress on the cantilever arms. Whilst McLure was on his

way back from New York on 29 August, the south arm and part of the central section collapsed into the St Lawrence River. Of more than 85 workmen on the structure at the time (who were within a quarter of an hour of finishing their shift for the day), all but 11 perished in the disaster that left behind a fragile-looking, mangled mass of iron. It was the end of Cooper's career.

A NEW BRIDGE
The second attempt at building the bridge involved a change of design, with a wider central drop-in truss, and two and a half times more steel was used. The suspended span was at 195m (640ft) almost twice as long as that on the Forth Rail Bridge. Painstaking checks were made to ensure the materials were strong enough this time; the bottom chords were made larger and of nickel alloy steel rather than carbon steel. However, a casting failed in one of the four rocker arms as the central span was being lifted into place. The structure had only been raised 3.5m (11.5ft) when it slipped and fell into the river, claiming the lives of 11 more workmen. Finally, a year later, a new centre span was successfully raised.

GALLOPING GERTIE
One of North America's other notorious bridge disasters was the Tacoma Narrows in Washington State, a plate girder suspension bridge designed by Leon Moisseiff and opened in July 1940. Handsome and slender, it soon gained the nickname 'Galloping Gertie' because of the alarming swaying and rippling motion of the main deck, a movement set off by even gentle breezes. The ripples would often be of such magnitude as to create hidden dips as motorists drove across. Engineers sought a solution to the problem, and added more stays. However, on 7 November 1940, a 68kph (42mph) wind proved its death knell. Aerodynamically unable to cope with the conditions, the bridge whipped up, twisted and disintegrated, remarkably with no loss of life apart from a motorist's dog. A cameraman was on hand to record the entire event for posterity.

Right The Tacoma Narrows Bridge in its final violent death throes before collapsing. Tubby, a cocker spaniel who dutifully refused to leave the bridge was the only casualty of the disaster.

COVERED BRIDGES

In their own rather humble, understated way, covered wooden bridges, in their numerous colours and forms, have almost come to epitomise small-town America. Built throughout the 19th and early 20th centuries and found in back roads where they are still used by traffic, many have fallen into neglect and without the enthusiasm of local conservationists could have disappeared.

Name	Hartland Bridge
Location	Hartland, Canada
Crosses	St. John River
Type	Wooden covered bridge
Function	Road bridge
Length	390m (1,280ft)
Completed	1921
Design	Hartland Bridge Company

THE NEEDS OF EXPANSION

After the American Declaration of Independence in 1776, America began to expand westwards rather than focusing its activities on the east coast and trading with Europe. A spate of bridge building ensued as the need emerged to cross great rivers. Many craftsmen from those pioneering days had brought with them a knowledge of European carpentry techniques and they turned to its plentiful supply of timber to build bridges – the US was scarcely an industrial nation at this stage, and iron parts were not used in bridges until the 1840s. The first major wooden bridge is believed to have been constructed by Enoch Hale in 1785 over the Connecticut River at Bellows Falls, Vermont.

It extended some 90m (295ft) across, with a central wooden pier on an islet, and was in existence until 1840.

THE FIRST COVERED BRIDGE

The main idea of covering a bridge was to shield the timber structure itself from the elements. Covered structures also screened the view to prevent horses and cattle from taking fright as they crossed over a river. In 1805, Timothy Palmer of Connecticut built the first covered bridge in the United States. It was a timber triple span, the Permanent Bridge over the Schuylkill River, Philadelphia – which might otherwise have become the site of political philosopher Thomas Paine's proposed iron bridge (see

Left The longest covered bridge in the world at Hartland was actually built as an uncovered structure in 1901. The roof was added following structural repairs in the 1920s.

215

COVERED BRIDGES

page 122). A member of the bridge company, Judge Richard Peters, had suggested the wooden bridge's life could be extended by adding a roof. In the event the bridge lasted 70 years until destruction by fire in 1875.

The following year, Palmer built his next covered bridge between Easton in Pennslyvania to Phillipsburg in New Jersey. Soon, covered bridges began to appear all over the northeast, and eventually across the United States and Canada. Some 20 various truss designs evolved, the earliest of them based on a simple kingpost truss – a pattern developed from medieval timber-frame building techniques, with a vertical kingpost between two diagonal supports. Later designs allowed for greater spans, some named after their inventors. The Town Truss, which appeared from 1820, was a simple lattice that could be easily and quickly assembled, while the Burr Truss (1815) combined a truss with two arches that rested on the abutments.

PRESERVATION AND NOSTALGIA

Of thousands of covered bridges that were erected, only a fraction have survived decades of neglect and often wilful damage: the fact that hundreds still exist is to a great extent attributable to a concerted effort by bands of enthusiasts wishing to preserve them. The National Society for the Preservation of Covered Bridges, founded in 1950, saved many covered bridges from demolition and publishes a worldwide list of all such spans, many of which in the United States are now listed on the National Register of Historic Places. Public opinion changed, regional highway authorities were persuaded, and it became accepted that covered bridges should in principle be retained, using traditional materials. Even so, the decline continued. In 1959, there were 1,344 19th and early 20th-century covered wooden bridges in the US; within 30 years, nearly a third had been lost to demolition, neglect and arson.

During the 1990s the nostalgic and romantic public affection for covered bridges was both captured and reinforced by the immensely popular *The Bridges of Madison County*, a 1992 novel by Robert James Waller, filmed in 1995 with Clint Eastwood and Meryl Streep. Eastwood portrays a photographer taking pictures of covered bridges in Iowa for *National Geographic* magazine in 1965. Six of Madison County's original 19 covered bridges remain today, and all are listed on the National Register of Historic Places.

In New England, Vermont has the richest concentration of covered bridges of any area. The longest in the United States crosses 151 metres from Vermont to New Hampshire between the towns of Windsor and Cornish. Pennsylvania has more covered bridges (over 200) than any other state, while the Hartland Bridge over the St. John River in Hartland, New Brunswick, spans 390m (1,280ft) and is the world's longest covered bridge still standing. Opened in 1901, it was designated a National Historic Site in 1980. The longest covered bridge ever built stretched 1,955m (6,414ft) over the Susquehanna River between Columbia and Wrightsville, Pennsylvania.

ACROSS THE WORLD

Some settlers in the New World would have seen covered wooden bridges built in earlier times in Europe. Early examples include the Kapellbrücke in Switzerland (see page 106), Lovech, in Bulgaria (built 1874, rebuilt 1982) and Ponte Coperto in Pavia, Italy (built 1354, replaced following damage by Allied action during the Second World War). They are unlikely, however, to have seen far more elaborate versions that are still to be found in China, particularly in the provinces of Guizhou and Fujian, where some spans sport spectacular multi-roofed structures.

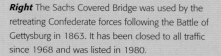

Left The town lattice truss bridge at Henniker, New Hampshire was constructed in 1972 by Milton Graton using traditional methods. Almost 42m (138ft) in length, it spans the Contoocook River.

Right The Sachs Covered Bridge was used by the retreating Confederate forces following the Battle of Gettysburg in 1863. It has been closed to all traffic since 1968 and was listed in 1980.

Name	Sachs Covered Bridge
Location	Gettysburg
Crosses	Marsh Creek
Type	Wooden covered bridge
Function	Road bridge (disused)
Length	Approx 30m (98ft)
Completed	1852
Design	David S. Stoner

GEORGE WASHINGTON BRIDGE

NEW YORK AND NEW JERSEY / USA

The Swiss architect Le Corbusier greatly admired the machine aesthetic of this, 'the most beautiful bridge in the world'. Writing 15 years after its opening, he observed 'It is the only seat of grace in the disordered city... the two towers rise so high that it brings you happiness'.

Name	George Washington Bridge
Location	New York and New Jersey
Crosses	Hudson River
Type	Suspension bridge
Function	Freeway and pedestrian bridge
Main span	1,067m (3501ft)
Length	1,451m (4,761ft)
Clearance	65m (213ft)
Opened	1931
Design	Othmar H. Ammann, assisted by Cass Gilbert

218

A STATELY ADDITION TO THE SKYLINE

Linking the west side of Manhattan with New Jersey, this double-deck, gravity anchored steel suspension span is one of the world's busiest bridges, serving the freeways I-95, US-1, and US-9 and carrying around 300,000 vehicles a day. At the time of building, the main span was twice the length of that found on any other suspension bridge in the world.

Initially named the Hudson River Bridge it become known informally as the GW Bridge, the GWB or the George. For six years, it was the world's longest suspension bridge until the opening of San Francisco's Golden Gate Bridge in 1937 (see page 232).

The 183-metre (600-foot) towers contain more than 43,000 tonnes of steel and were a prominent and stately addition to the New York skyline, as tall as many skyscrapers. They were originally intended to be clad in concrete with granite facing, but they were left in their naked steel form which earned widespread approval for its appearance and because it saved money in hard times in the wake of the Wall Street Crash of 1929.

OTHMAR AMMANN

In 1906 the governors of New York and New Jersey had proposed a bridge here, over the Hudson River between 179th Street in Manhattan and Fort Lee, at a relatively narrow point. Ten years later Gustav Lindenthal put forward the idea

of a railway bridge from midtown Manhattan to New Jersey, but Othmar Ammann – who became the chief engineer of the bi-state Port Authority – argued this plan was too expensive and would be too difficult to realise in congested midtown Manhattan. Ammann's own scheme for a road bridge was to be located between high points on the shores of Manhattan and New Jersey giving adequate clearance for ships. He found a supporter in Governor George Silzer of New Jersey, and approval was

Right The bridge crosses the Hudson River and connects the Washington Heights area of Manhattan in New York to Fort Lee in New Jersey. Four roads – the I-95, US 1 & 9 and the US 46 – can all be found on the bridge.

GEORGE WASHINGTON BRIDGE

given, with Ammann as bridge designer and chief engineer, with the assistance of the architect Cass Gilbert, whose most famous New York work was the Woolworth Building.

RESISTANCE THROUGH WEIGHT

Although the design used conventional suspension cables and slender steel towers, it had a radical innovation in dispensing with stiffening trusses that had been used in earlier suspension bridges to support massive loads such as railways. Steel technology had now advanced to a point where Ammann saw that the steel frame would be adequate to carry the dead and live loads. He calculated that the weight of the deck and cables in themselves provided sufficient resistance to winds. The solidity of Ammann's bridge was demonstrated in 1965 when a private plane crashed into it, fortuitously leaving both bridge and pilot unscathed – just a year after Ammann's last New York bridge, the Verrazano-Narrows Bridge opened (see page 226).

The construction, carried out in the lean years of the Great Depression, progressed briskly, although 12 workers lost their lives. It was completed on 25 October, 1931, eight months ahead of schedule. A far-sighted element in the design was the inclusion of space for an extra truss-stiffened deck that could be added when the demands of vehicle traffic increased. This was duly inserted some 4.5m (15ft) below the original

deck in 1962, 31 years after the bridge opened. The construction work began in 1959 and adhered to the original design; it was carried out without interruption to the eight traffic lanes on the traffic deck above by means of the raising of 76 structural steel sections from the river. The additional deck increased the capacity of the bridge by 75 per cent, making it the only 14-lane suspension bridge in the world.

THE LIGHTHOUSE AND THE BRIDGE

Beneath the upper arch of the New Jersey tower drapes the world's largest free-flying American flag, measuring 18m x 27m (59ft x 89ft); its stripes are approximately 1.5m (5ft) wide and the stars measure about 1.2m (4ft) in diameter. Weather permitting, the flag is flown on eight public holidays. Beneath the Manhattan tower stands a small lighthouse, erected in New Jersey in 1880 and re-erected on its present site in 1921, this operated for 26 years. Its proposed demolition in 1951 caused a wave of protest among the public, who remembered it from *The Little Red Lighthouse and the Great Gray Bridge* (1942), a perennially popular children's story by Hildegarde Swift. It is now preserved as a New York City landmark and listed on the National Register of Historic Places. Exactly half a century after its opening, the George Washington Bridge was designated a National Historic Civil Engineering Landmark by the American Society of Civil Engineers in 1981.

Left In 1932 (its first full year in operation) 5.5 million vehicles were estimated to have crossed the one-deck structure. Today, approximately 108 million vehicles a year make the journey.

Right The double-decker suspension bridge; 8 lanes of traffic run across the top deck, whilst a lower deck, opened in 1962, has room for a further 6 lanes. A sidewalk provides access for walkers and cyclists.

BROOKLYN BRIDGE

NEW YORK / USA

The Brooklyn Bridge is as much a New York landmark as the Statue of Liberty or the Empire State Building. The largest suspension bridge in the world for its first 20 years, this structural and architectural triumph cost many lives in its construction – including that of its designer.

FORTUNATE AERODYNAMICS

The bridge features an elevated walkway, a four-lane road and an elevated railway; the latter ceased operating in 1944. Four massive 38-centimetre (1.2ft) thick cables hold the road and rail lines high above the river. The 90.5-metre (269-foot) Gothic granite and limestone towers with their arched portals support the cables by means of saddles that sit at the top of each tower and help to absorb the load and shift in the structure caused by the wind, traffic movement and temperature. A total of 15,200 vertical suspenders are strung down to the bridge floor, with 400 diagonal stays radiating down from the towers. More than 23,000km (14.3 miles) of wire was used for the suspender ropes. The use of a stiffening truss structure withstands any cross winds;

this feature was by fortune rather than by design, as the aerodynamics of large bridges like this was an area of engineering not understood when the bridge was built.

Until Brooklyn Bridge was completed in 1883, the ferry was the only way across between Manhattan and Brooklyn. The desire for a fixed link across the East River – more a tidal strait than a true river – required a single span to cross high above the ship masts, to pit engineering ingenuity against the forces of nature.

JOHN AUGUSTUS ROEBLING

The great idea germinated in 1855 from the German-born bridge designer John Augustus Roebling, who had designed suspension bridges along the Delaware, Niagara and

Left In its planning stages, the structure was called the New York and Brooklyn Bridge but gained its shortened name following a letter to the editor of the *Brooklyn Daily Eagle* in 1867.

Ohio Rivers, and had supervised waterway schemes in Pennsylvania; his Delaware Aqueduct of 1848 is the oldest existing suspension bridge in the USA. Fourteen years earlier Roebling had invented the twisted wire-rope cable, which was capable of bearing immensely heavy loads, and in 1847 set up his own wire-rope cable factory. He conceived a plan to replace the ferry between Manhattan and Brooklyn with a massive bridge 'to be ranked as a national monument... a great work of art.'

WORK BEGINS

Roebling found support from a Brooklyn businessman William Kingsley, and state senator Henry Murphy put the legal machinery in motion permitting the New York Bridge Company to build a bridge here and to extract tolls. He was appointed as the chief engineer for the project in 1867. This was to be the first ever use of steel instead of iron for use in bridge cables; Roebling argued that steel was less susceptible to oscillation caused by winds. In August 1876 a temporary wire footbridge joined the two anchorages across the East River for

the first time. The following February 1877 work began on spinning the four cables. The suspending ropes and deck beams were installed in place, followed by the diagonal stays and the stiffening trusses.

THE CURSE OF CAISSONS

It was while surveying the site for one of the granite towers that Roebling had his foot crushed by a ferry, and died of tetanus before construction began. His son Washington Roebling continued work on the design, but suffered from caissons disease (also known as the 'the bends') that had fatally struck many workers who used the pneumatic caissons (pressurised working chambers at the foot of the piers) during construction. Roebling was left partially paralysed until his death in 1926, although he remained very active intellectually. He retreated to a nearby apartment and conducted the works from there from 1873 to 1877, assisted by his wife Emily who took an increasingly leading role, becoming proficient at mathematics and bridge engineering and making daily visits to oversee the workers.

In all nearly 30 of the 600-strong workforce died during the construction. The grim conditions of the caissons accounted for most of these; two others died falling from the towers, and another was decapitated when the cable was being installed.

A NEW FEATURE ON THE SKYLINE

When the bridge was officially opened on 23 May, 1883 in front of a crowd of thousands, Emily Roebling took the first ride over. The structure's appearance on the New York skyline was a sensation – in that pre-skyscraper era the towers dwarfed virtually any other structure in sight. However, misfortune continued to dog the structure: six days after the opening, a woman tripped on the approach and her screams led to a stampede among the crowd of people on the bridge who believed the structure was collapsing; 12 died in the panic and many more were injured. But the bridge has since proved immensely well built. In 1884, the circus owner Phineas Barnum demonstrated its solidity by parading across it with a herd of 21 elephants. In 1964 the bridge was designated a National Historic Landmark.

Name	Brooklyn Bridge
Location	New York
Crosses	East River
Type	Cable-stayed steel suspension bridge with masonry towers
Function	Road, rail and pedestrian
Main span	486m (1,597ft)
Length	1,834m (6017ft)
Clearance	41m (135ft)
Opened	1883
Design	John Augustus Roebling

Left A Circle Line tourist boat passes under the bridge. The nearby Manhattan Bridge (see background) was opened in 1909 and connects Lower Manhattan with Brooklyn at the Flatbush Avenue Extension.

Right The bridge has always featured a pedestrian walkway; following the terrorist attacks of 11 September 2001, many people left Manhattan by this route after the subway service was suspended.

VERRAZANO-NARROWS BRIDGE

NEW YORK / USA

With a suspended span just longer than that of the Golden Gate Bridge, the Verrazano-Narrows Bridge represented the latest achievement of a century of US suspension bridge-building. The heaviest suspension bridge ever built, it carries 12 lanes of traffic on two decks

INTERSTATE LINK

The bridge provided a new gateway to New York Harbour, with 66 metres of clearance to allow through the cruise and container ships using the ports of New York and New Jersey. Connecting the borough of Brooklyn with Staten Island, it is an important link in the interstate highway system that links Brooklyn, Long Island and Manhattan. It is sited on The Narrows, the tidal strait at the entrance to the harbour, which was guarded by historic forts on each side. Following a campaign by the Italian Historical Society of America, the bridge was named the Verrazano-Narrows Bridge after Giovanni da Verrazano, the Italian explorer. An alternative proposal was to name it after

President John F. Kennedy, assassinated the year before it opened, but that honour went to the New York international airport, formerly Idlewild.

EXPOSED TO THE ELEMENTS

The bridge was the last project of Othmar Ammann (1879–1965), who between the 1930s and the 1960s designed six of New York city's major crossings. Of these, it is the bridge most exposed to the elements, because of its height and its location close to the open sea, and it occasionally needs to close in high winds and blizzards. Hot temperatures affecting the steel cables can make the double-decked roadway sink by 3.5m (11.9ft) in summer.

Name	Verrazano-Narrows Bridge
Crosses	New York Harbour
Type	Suspension bridge
Function	Road bridge
Main span	1,298m (4,259ft)
Length	1.6 km (1 mile)
Clearance	66m (217ft)
Height	207m (679ft)
Opened	1964
Design	Othmar Ammann

Far left The Verrazano-Narrows Bridge connects Fort Hamilton in Brooklyn with Fort Wadsworth in Staten Island. When it opened in 1964, it was the longest suspension span in the world.

MACKINAC BRIDGE

The Straits of Mackinac, between the Upper and Lower peninsulas of the US State of Michigan, are so prone to gales and ice that running a year-round ferry service was impossible. A bridge had been proposed since the 1880s, while other solutions including a 'floating tunnel' and a series of causeways linking up islands were also considered. Feasibility studies for a bridge started in the mid 1930s, though work was put on hold until after the Second World War. Eventually, designer David Steinman was appointed in 1953 and the bridge opened in 1958. With the 1940 collapse of the Tacoma Narrows Bridge (see page 213) in mind, Steinman took exceptional measures to ensure the stability of his suspension bridge design. The cables were specified with a huge safety margin, the massive pier foundations were sunk into rock more than 60m (197ft) below the water level and stiffening trusses projected 3m (9.8ft) either side of

the vehicle deck to help to break up the force of high winds hitting it. The roadway also has an aerofoil shape to provide lift in a cross wind, while at its centre the two traffic lanes are made of open grids which allow upward airflow to cancel the lifting effect.

The unusually long side spans gave the Mackinac bridge the world record for the longest suspension bridge overall when it was built, at 2,626 metres, though it did not have the longest central span. The record for overall length for a suspension bridge is now held by the Akashi-Kaikyo Bridge in Japan (3,909m (12,825ft), see page 186).

Right A 21 metre-wide stiffening truss hangs unfinished from a pier of the Mackinac Bridge. The inclusion of the trusses to support the roadway and deck was a lesson learnt from the collapse of the Tacoma Narrows Bridge.

227

NEW RIVER GORGE BRIDGE

WEST VIRGINIA / **USA**

One of the great sights of the Appalachian mountains, this steel arch crosses high above the whitewater rapids of the New River. The highest road crossing in the United States, until the opening of the Millau Viaduct, it was the highest road crossing in the world.

EXTREME SPORTS

Over six hours on the third Saturday each October, hundreds of participants and up to 80,000 spectators home in on this structure for Bridge Day, when hundreds of BASE (Building, Antenna, Span and Earth) jumpers – sky-divers who launch themselves from fixed points rather than from planes – come to parachute into the gorge. It is billed as the largest extreme sports event in the world, and takes place at a time when the autumn colours of the mixed hardwood forest are often at their most vibrant.

For the rest of the year, the bridge serves as a four-lane road bridge for US Highway 19. With its opening, a trip that previously entailed snaking down and up tortuous roads was instantly cut from around 45 minutes to less than a minute.

BUILDING AT HEIGHT

The depth of the gorge meant that constructing piers was unfeasible; the bridge would have to cross in a single span – either as a suspension or an arch bridge. The design chosen by Michael Baker was for a single steel arch bridge founded in the solid rock either side of the gorge. The height of the pylons needed for a suspension bridge would have interfered with local aviation.

To begin construction, cables were strung 1,070m (3,510ft) across the New River gorge between 100-metre tall temporary towers. Trolleys were run along the cables to position the steel sections, all designed with an open truss construction to minimise wind resistance and made in weathering steel that eventually creates a rust-like appearance which blends in with the yellows, oranges and russets of the autumn foliage and never needs painting. In the history of long-span steel arch bridge engineering, this was the first time that computerised calculations were relied on to the extent that the two halves of the arch fitted perfectly when they were joined, rather than having a gap which needed closing. Construction took three years, at a cost of $37 million US.

RECORD BREAKER

The New River Gorge Bridge was the world's longest single arch steel span, until pushed into second place by the opening of the Lupu Bridge (see page 172) over the Huangpu River in Shanghai, which has a span of 550m (1,805ft). It is also the second highest bridge in the United States after the Royal Gorge Bridge over the Arkansas River in Colorado – which was built in 1929 and which at 321m (1,053ft) above the river is the highest suspension bridge over water in the world.

Name	New River Gorge Bridge
Location	West Virginia, USA
Crosses	New River
Type	Single steel arch bridge
Function	Road bridge
Main span	518m (1,700ft)
Length	923m (3,032ft)
Clearance	267m (863ft)
Opened	1978
Design	Michael Baker

Right Built between 1974 and 1977, the bridge was finally opened in 1978. It is located near Fayetteville, West Virginia and carries US Highway 19 which connects Lake Erie with the Gulf of Mexico.

LAKE PONTCHARTRAIN CAUSEWAY BRIDGE

LOUISIANA / USA

The two parallel bridges of the Lake Pontchartrain Causeway are deceptively modest in appearance, with their simple repeated concrete beam spans of as little as 17m (55.8ft) apiece. In fact they are the world's longest bridges measured by length.

ORIGINS OF THE CAUSEWAY

The idea of a Lake Pontchartrain crossing dates back to the early 19th century. As the lake is relatively shallow, averaging only 3 to 5m (9.8 to 16.4ft), in the 1920s an idea developed of dredging the bottom to form a series of islands from north to south, linked by bridges. This would have had the added benefit of creating saleable land for holiday houses, and several plots are even said to have been sold without any work taking place. However, today's causeway derived from the new technology of pre-stressed concrete, first demonstrated in North America by the Walnut Street Bridge in Philadelphia, Pennsylvania (1949).

TWO BRIDGES

The first causeway's completion in 1956 represented a triumph of innovation. Over 2,000 separate 17-metre (56-foot) spans, pre-fabricated from reinforced concrete slabs, were positioned onto hollow pre-stressed concrete piles by a floating crane. Its opening reduced drive times into New Orleans by some 50 minutes, bringing Mandeville and the North Shore area into the metropolitan area. The second bridge, just 69m (226ft) longer, was installed 13 years later to a similar design but with longer spans. Now each carries two lanes of traffic across almost the widest part of Lake Pontchartrain, north of New Orleans.

The second bridge took just over 18 months to build, using even more efficient methods. The piles were strengthened to support spans of 25m (82ft) rather than 17m (56ft), and at times the spans were being produced at a rate of 20 a week. The roadway incorporates two bascule openings of 7.6 and 15m (25 and 49ft).

HURRICANE FORCES

On three occasions sections have collapsed after barge collisions, but the causeway has never been seriously damaged by hurricanes. After Hurricane Katrina of 2005 put another main Lake Pontchartrain crossing, the I-10 Twin Span Bridge, out of action, the undamaged causeway was taken over by the emergency services and became a key route for the relief effort.

In 2002, the Causeway Commission had considered building a third causeway, but decided to refurbish the existing structures as studies showed that traffic growth was levelling off. However, as a result of the 2005 hurricane, there has been a population shift to the north of the lake, and an increase in vehicle traffic. The third causeway plan is being re-examined as it would cater for the increased demand, and would provide a better evacuation route to the north if another disaster occurred on a similar scale.

Name	Lake Pontchartrain Causeway
Location	Louisiana
Crosses	Lake Pontchartrain
Type	Concrete bridge
Function	Road bridge
Main span	2,170 17-metre (56-ft) spans
Length	38km (23.6 miles)
Clearance	4.6m (15ft)
Height	18m (59ft)
Opened	1956 and 1969
Design	Palmer and Baker, Inc.

Left The causeway connects Metairie, a suburb of New Orleans to the city of Mandeville in Louisiana.

CAUSEWAY OR BRIDGE?

Although universally known as 'The Causeway' to New Orleans locals, the Pontchartrain crossing is more a low bridge than a causeway. Typically, a causeway consists of a raised road or railway supported by an earth or concrete bank, rather than by the spans of a bridge or viaduct. However, when the bank includes openings or culverts for water to pass through, the distinction becomes blurred. It is their inaccessibility to shipping that is the main disadvantage of causeways, along with possible effects on currents and silting, and a tendency to become dangerous during storms as their decks are so close to the water. However, they can incorporate a central spanned section to allow boats through.

In Britain, there is evidence for wooden causeways dating back thousands of years, preserved in the peaty waters of the Somerset Levels and the Cambridgeshire Fens. The Sweet Track, discovered in 1970 near Glastonbury, ran some 2km (1.2 miles) across a swamp between an island and higher ground. Its walkway consisted of oak planks laid end-to-end over supports of crossed ash, oak and lime poles that were driven into the waterlogged soil. The tree-ring sequences on the timbers have been dated very precisely to the Neolithic period, 3807 to 3806BC.

At Flag Fen, near Peterborough (UK), a 1.5-km (0.9-mile) long wooden causeway and platform from the Late Bronze Age, built between about 1350 and 950BC, was discovered in the peat fens; much of it is preserved underwater at the Flag Fen Bronze Age Centre. It is estimated that the construction used around 60,000 timber uprights and 250,000 horizontal planks over the centuries. Many metal, stone and bone objects have been found, deliberately placed within or alongside the structure, including fine metal objects that have been deliberately broken. The British climate became colder and wetter in the Late Bronze Age, and some believe that these were ritual offerings made to placate the waters.

GOLDEN GATE BRIDGE

SAN FRANCISCO / **UNITED STATES**

Now an internationally recognised symbol, the Golden Gate Bridge was completed in 1937, and at the time was the longest suspension bridge span in the world. It had faced fierce opposition from the world's largest ferry company, and might never have been built had it not been backed by the emerging US automobile industry.

Name	Golden Gate Bridge
Location	San Francisco
Crosses	Golden Gate Strait
Type	Suspension bridge
Function	Road and railway bridge
Span	1,280m (4,200ft)
Length	2,737m (8,980ft)
Clearance	67m (220ft)
Opened	27 May 1937
Design	Joseph B. Strauss, Charles Alton Ellis and Irving Morrow

UNSHACKLING GROWTH

By the 1920s San Francisco was the largest American city still reliant on ferry boats: many felt that economic growth was being held back by the lack of any permanent links with the surrounding settlements. However, others argued that a bridge would be unfeasible because of the width of the Golden Gate Strait, the strength of the tides and the ferocious winds and dense fogs. Moreover, the site was virtually at the epicentre of the San Andreas Fault, source of the massive earthquake which had devastated the city in 1906. Meanwhile, the Golden Gate Ferry company had an effective monopoly on links between San Francisco and Marin County. The alternative, going by land around the bay meant a trip of several hundred kilometres. The ferry owners filed a lawsuit against the bridge proposal, provoking a mass boycott of the ferries. Against them stood the fledgling automobile industry, which was promoting the development of new bridges and roads to help to increase the demand for cars.

WORKING WITH STRAUSS

After more than a decade of campaigning for the project, Joseph B. Strauss was chosen as the chief engineer. He had brought the project to fruition through his energy and political skill, but had little experience

Right The Golden Gate Bridge connects San Francisco on the northern tip of the city's peninsula to Marin County (in the foreground).

of designing at this scale – his expertise being in small drawbridges. Charles Alton Ellis, a professor of structural and bridge engineering at the University of Illinois, consulting remotely with bridge designer Leon Moisseiff, was responsible for the bulk of the technical and theoretical calculations underpinning the design, but received no credit at the time. Strauss dismissed him in 1931, supposedly for wasting money on telegram exchanges with Moisseiff. Ellis is said to have continued working unpaid on the project through the Depression; settling back into academic life, he always kept a picture of the bridge above his desk.

CREATING A WORK OF ART

The overall look of the bridge, described by one observer as 'the world's largest art deco sculpture', was mainly the work of consulting architect Irving Morrow. He chose the detail on the streetlamps, railings and walkways, created the 227-metre (745-foot) pylons, with their art deco stepped outlines, and selected the distinctive colour. This was originally a red lead-based finish known as International Orange, chosen to blend well with the natural surroundings yet make the bridge visible in fog.

Construction took more than four years, starting with the north pier which, fortuitously, could be anchored in solid bedrock only 6m (20ft) below the water. The south pier, virtually in the open sea, proved more difficult as conditions were too rough for barges: an access trestle running more than a third of a kilometre out into the water had to be built so access could be achieved. Cable spinning began in August 1935: each of the 7,125-tonne cables consisted of over 27,000 wires which were built up 24 wires at a time by being strung across the water and back again by continuously travelling wheels. The deck sections then had to be built outwards from both sides of each tower at the same time, in order to balance their weight.

ELEMENTS AND EARTHQUAKES

The bridge needed to withstand gales and ocean currents as well as the risk of earthquakes, and to have a higher clearance than ever achieved before in order to accommodate ocean-going shipping. The suspended deck of 213m (699ft) required a stiffening truss, but this was the shallowest yet provided in relation to the deck length. This proved basically sound, but in time high winds caused an unnerving rippling effect and 4,700 tonnes of bracing were added across the underside to stabilise the deck. Moisseiff's later design for the Tacoma Narrows Bridge took his idea of a flexible deck to reduce overall stress on the structure too far: it was too narrow, collapsing in 1940 after only a few months' service.

Approximately 200,000 pedestrians and roller skaters flocked onto the bridge on its first day of opening. It has been closed only five times due to high winds in its 70-year history; In 1982 the wind was enough to set the structure in visible motion. The San Francisco bay area also remains vulnerable to earthquakes and although the bridge has yet to be structurally damaged the overall structure has been modified so it can better respond to strong motions (including earthquakes) without damage.

GOLDEN GATE BRIDGE

AN ALARMING OCCUPATION

Construction worker Albert 'Frenchy' Gales was among a dozen or so men trapped at the top of the unfinished south tower during an earthquake in 1935. He recalled that the tower swung some 5m (16ft) each way: 'The whole thing would sway toward the ocean, guys would say, "here we go!" Then it would sway back toward the bay'. In fact he was probably safer than most previous bridge workmen. Strauss had introduced the use of movable safety netting; those who fell and survived joined what became known informally as the 'Halfway to Hell Club'.

Right During construction, Joseph Strauss pioneered the use of movable safety nets which saved many workmen from a fate in the choppy waters of the bay.

Left Irving Morrow chose the now famous International Orange colour of the Golden Gate. The paint is formulated to help to protect the bridge against rust caused by the frequent fogs that envelop the structure.

SAN FRANCISCO-OAKLAND BAY BRIDGE

SAN FRANCISCO / USA

San Francisco was transformed in the 1930s by the opening of this crossing, the largest and most expensive bridge project of its age, as audacious as the Golden Gate Bridge under construction across the city at the same time and perhaps an even greater undertaking.

A MATTER OF GEOGRAPHY

San Francisco's peninsula location meant it was perfectly placed to prosper from the shipping trade during the California Gold Rush of the mid 19th century. However, with the arrival of the first cross-US trains in 1868 it found itself cut off from the railhead by deep water. A link was clearly needed, and a Bay Bridge Committee was formed as early as 1872. The self-styled Emperor Norton I, a San Francisco eccentric immortalised by the writings of Mark Twain, threatened to have the city fathers arrested by his private army if they did not take the plan forward. For decades, however, the Bay was considered too wide and too deep, and with time the requirements changed. By the 1920s, not only a railway bridge but a road crossing was required. Plans for an underwater tube were abandoned as inadequate for the growing volume of automobile traffic.

THE TWO-BRIDGE SOLUTION

Eventually the bridge came into being during the post-1929 Great Depression, supported by President Hoover as an economic reconstruction project. Technical challenges abounded; the site was in an earthquake zone, among deep and fast-flowing waters, and prone to strong gusty winds. The complex solution was the huge twin-span suspension West Span over the deep waters near San Francisco, and the cantilevered East Span, with its extensive truss bridge and causeway approaches, over the shallow mudflats on the Oakland Side. The two contrasting bridges were joined

by a double-deck tunnel through the rocky Yerba Buena Island – at the time the largest-diameter bore tunnel ever constructed – to accommodate the road and rail crossings one above the other (as they existed on the bridges).

The West Span required a massive artificial anchorage point. The resulting central tower was taller than any building in San Francisco at the time, with foundations constructed in waters up to 30m (98ft) deep. This was beyond the depth at which men could safely work in a pumped-dry chamber using compressed air, so the massive caissons had to be built on a slipway, launched, towed into position and then sunk onto an irregular and sloping surface of rock.

HEAVY LOADS

During its first year, there were nine million vehicle crossings of the bridge, far more than had been expected. By 1950 this had increased three fold and in 1958 the rail tracks were converted to carry additional traffic lanes.

The 1989 Loma Prieta Earthquake badly damaged a section of the East Span. Fifteen metres (49ft) of upper deck collapsed onto the deck below and the whole crossing was closed for weeks. A massive seismic refit operation is now under way, designed to ensure that the bridge can re-open within 24 hours of a major earthquake. The West Span has been reinforced, while the East Span is being replaced by what will be the world's longest single tower, self-anchored

suspension bridge. In this design, intended to complement the West Span and the Golden Gate Bridge, there is only one main cable. This is anchored to the deck at the eastern end, wrapped over the tower, around the western end, and back over the tower to the eastern end again. Linker beams between the four legs of the tower, designed to break in an earthquake, will absorb much of the impact. When it opens parallel traffic lanes will run under an angled canopy of suspension cables and the original East Span will be demolished.

Right The western span consists of a suspension bridge. Both halves of the bridge are connected to the Yerba Buena tunnel which when built was the largest diameter tunnel in the world.

Above The eastern span between Yerba Buena Island and Oakland consists of a double-tower cantilever bridge.

Name	San Francisco–Oakland Bay Bridge East Span
Location	San Francisco
Crosses	San Francisco Bay
Type	Cantilever bridge and truss bridge
Function	Road bridge
Span	427m (1,401ft)
Length	2.1km (1.3 miles)
Clearance	58m (190ft)
Opened	12 November 1936
Design	Ralph Modjeski

Name	San Francisco-Oakland Bay Bridge West Span
Location	San Francisco
Crosses	San Francisco Bay
Type	Suspension bridge
Function	Road bridge
Span	Two 704-metre (2,310-foot) suspension spans
Length	2.8km (1.7 miles)
Clearance	67m (220ft)
Opened	12 November 1936
Design	Ralph Modjeski

SUNSHINE SKYWAY BRIDGE

FLORIDA / **USA**

The graceful Skyway, the world's longest cable-stayed concrete bridge, has a sail-like arrangement of cable stays that allude to Florida's nickname, the 'Sunshine State'. The story behind it is anything but sunny: it was built in the wake of one of the worst-ever American bridge disasters.

EMERGENCY STOPPING ONLY

DANGEROUS WATERS

Tampa Bay is in one of the world's longest and most dangerous shipping channels, notorious for its shallow waters and extreme weather conditions. In 1987 the present Sunshine Skyway replaced two bridges that crossed Tampa Bay between St. Petersburg and Bradenton. The first of these opened in 1954, with long approach causeways and a steeply inclined cantilever-truss crossing the shipping channel. A second bridge, opened in 1971, doubled the traffic capacity and took southbound traffic.

On 9 May 1980, Captain John Lerro was sailing the freighter *Summit Venture* from the Gulf of Mexico along Tampa Bay to the Port of Tampa. The ship had no cargo and rode high in the water through patchy fog and rain before a tropical storm of ferocious intensity descended. Suddenly there was virtually no visibility, and the ship's radar failed just before Captain John Lerro reached the 1971 bridge, where he needed to make a 13-degree turn to take him between the two main piers. The vessel rammed into the southbound span, knocking out a large

Name	Sunshine Skyway Bridge
Location	Florida
Crosses	Tampa Bay
Type	Cable-stayed bridge
Function	Freeway bridge
Main span	366m (1,201ft)
Length	1,219.6m (4,001ft) (main bridge)
Total length	8.85km (5.5 miles)
Clearance	58.8m (193ft)
Opened	1987
Design	Figg & Muller Engineers

239

Left In 2006, the Florida Department of Transport started an overhaul of the bridge in response to criticisms of poor maintenance. This included stripping all the paint from the cables and repainting them all the same consistent yellow.

Above A car stops just 36cm (14 inches) short of plummetting into Tampa Bay following the destruction of the original bridge's roadway by the freighter *Summit Venture* during a storm in 1980.

section of roadway into the bay, and killing 35 people who were on the bridge – most of them on a Greyhound bus. Two people had miraculous escapes; a pickup driver's vehicle landed on the deck of the freighter and he swam to safety, and one motorist stopped his car just 35 centimetres from the drop. Captain Lerro was cleared of wrongdoing by a state grand jury.

For a period, the northbound span continued to take traffic, but in two directions as it had originally done. However, a decision was taken to replace both structures; the idea of a tunnel was unfeasible because of the high water table. Accordingly, a new Skyway was conceived and a huge demolition project was soon underway for the older structures, the approaches of which were made into the Skyway Fishing Pier State Park.

SAFETY ABOVE ALL

The new Skyway is modelled after the Brotonne Bridge over the River Seine

in France. It has nearly 15m (49ft) more clearance than its predecessors, and the width of the main span over the shipping channel has been increased by a third from 244 to 366m (801 to 1,201ft). An important safety feature system was designed by Parsons Brinkerhoff in the form of 36 large concrete islands (see image, right), which act as safety buffers and can withstand an impact from an 87,000-tonne tanker travelling at 10 knots. The 21 cables within their yellow tubes are flanked on either side by two lanes of roadway, so motorists can enjoy unimpeded views. The deck comprises more than 300 precast hollow concrete segments that can be entered for maintenance, as necessary when the steel within the precast concrete has corroded.

The Sunshine Skyway was officially renamed in 2005 as the Bob Graham Sunshine Skyway Bridge, after the former Florida governor who opted to replace the 1954 and 1971 cantilever spans with this radical design.

SEVEN-MILE BRIDGE

Another spectacular project by Figg & Muller Engineers in Florida is the Seven-Mile Bridge, one of several bridges on the US 1 Overseas Highway freeway linking the Florida Keys archipelago. Like its counterparts, it is constructed to withstand winds in excess of 360kph (224mph) in a region prone to hurricanes. It runs 10,931 metres, just short of seven miles, making it the longest continuous concrete segmental bridge in the world when completed in 1982, five years before the opening of the Sunshine Skyway. Also built to carry water pipes and telephone lines, it has 440 spans, and most of it is raised just above the level of the water. The central arc rises 20m (66ft) above sea level to allow clearance for shipping. Its superstructure is a post-tensioned box girder design, while the precast segmental piers are hollow and were quick to erect; the work was completed six months ahead of schedule. Most of the bridge's predecessor, opened 1912, is still in situ – being used by anglers, cyclists and sightseers. The rebuilding of Seven-Mile Bridge is commemorated each April by a marathon, during which the bridge is closed to traffic.

Left The Seven-Mile Bridge featured in the film *True Lies* (1994) where it was partly 'destroyed'. Film makers shot scenes on the bridge and used computer generated imagery and a 24-metre (80-foot) model to create the effects.

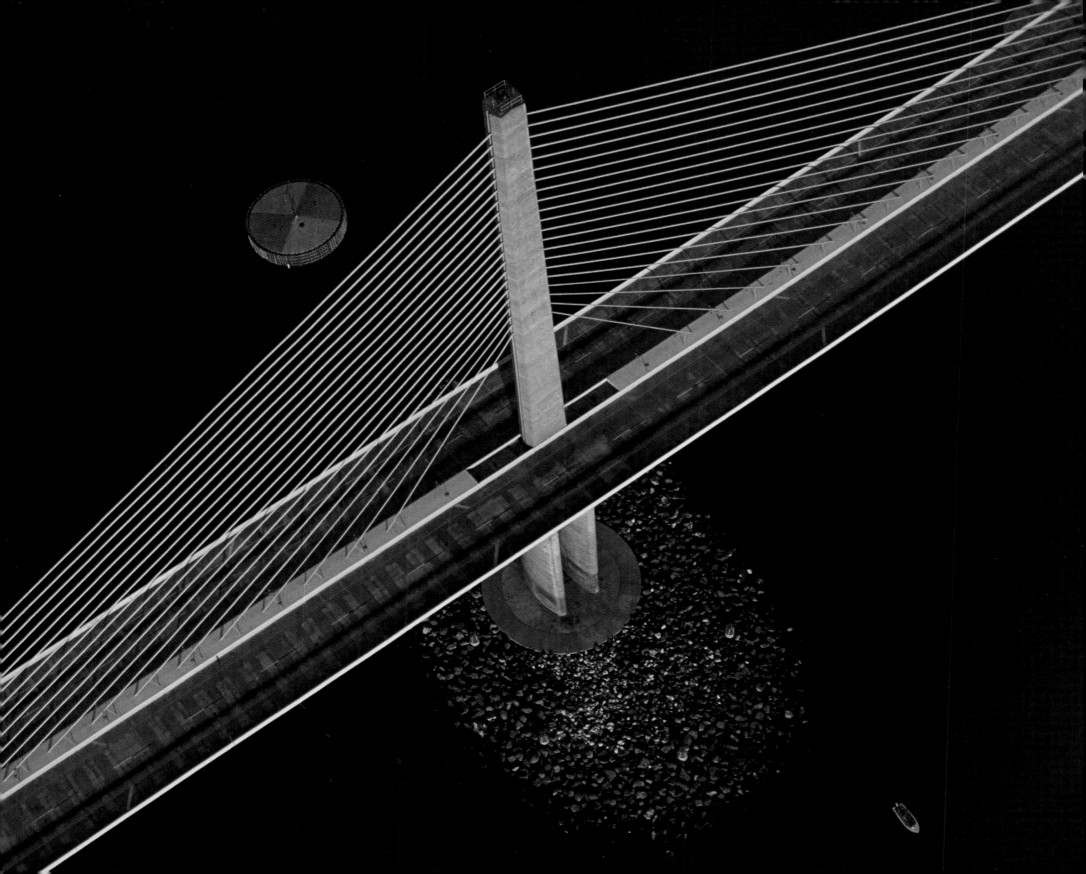

SOUTH AND CENTRAL AMERICA

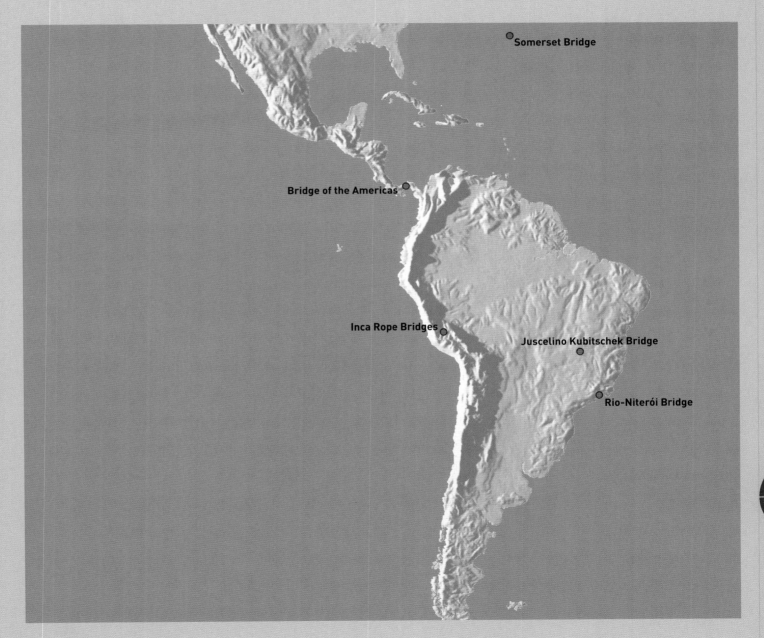

Somerset Bridge

Bridge of the Americas

Inca Rope Bridges

Juscelino Kubitschek Bridge

Rio-Niterói Bridge

Left A trekker crosses the Inca log bridge at Macchu Picchu in Peru.

BRIDGE OF THE AMERICAS

BALBOA / PANAMA

When it opened in 1914, the Panama Canal cut across one of the narrowest parts of the isthmus that joins North and South America to join the Atlantic and Pacific Oceans. It created a crucial route for shipping, yet divided Colón and Panama City from the rest of the Republic. The opening of what is now known as the Bridge of the Americas physically reunited the country – and two continents.

BRIDGING A LANDMARK

The Panama Canal was one of the largest and most difficult engineering projects of all time, built at a cost of some 27,500 lives. The first work on it was begun by the French in 1880, but it was the United States that finally completed its construction, and retained responsibility for the Panama Canal Zone from 1903 until 1979. The idea of building a fixed span over the waterway was first proposed in 1923, and over the years the Panamanian government put pressure on the US to build a crossing. Two swing bridges provided a means to cross the canal when there was no shipping along those sections, but these and various ferry services had soon proved inadequate. In 1955, a treaty committed the United States to building a bridge. Work began in 1959 and was completed seven years later.

INTO THE ZONE

The area of the Panama Canal Zone had physically cut Panama into two. Controlled by the US and used for military purposes for a great deal of its history, the zone had

its own civil government as well as its own police and courts system (American civilians born in the zone are still called 'Zonians' to this day). The problems caused by the existence of the area had become a serious political issue by the time of the opening of the bridge in 1962. Public opinion in Panama was against naming the structure after Maurice H. Thatcher and in favour of calling it the Bridge of the Americas. Thatcher had been the governor of the Canal Zone between 1910 and 1913 and was the longest-lived member of the Isthmian Canal Commission (the organisation set up to oversee the building of the Panama Canal). A demonstration was held by pro-Panamanian protesters who disrupted the proceedings of the inauguration by marching up and down the bridge. Violence erupted between the police and protesters who had removed commemorative plaques on the bridge.

CROSSING THE GAP

The bridge is a steel and concrete truss arch design, built across Panama Bay at the Pacific Canal entrance near Panama City. Construction was carried out from both shores, and on 16 May, 1962, the first 21-metre (75.4ft), 98-tonne steel beam was put into place to join the two sections at the middle. Initially, it was known as the

Thatcher Ferry Bridge – named after the 92-year-old former governor who cut the tape during the inauguration services. However, it was officially renamed the Bridge of the Americas in 1979 when Panama regained control of the area. The bridge was the first fixed structure uniting the continents of North and South America, and formed a part of the still-incomplete Pan-American Highway, proposed from Alaska to South America. A major practical and environmental obstacle to the realisation of this scheme is the Darién Gap, a swathe of rainforest between the Panama Canal and the Colombian border.

A SECOND BRIDGE

Increasing traffic congestion prompted the building of a second fixed bridge over the canal, the Centennial Bridge (Puente Centenario; named after Panama's centennial, on 3 November 2003), which opened in 2004 to carry six lanes of motorway traffic, and over which the Pan-American Highway has been rerouted. Designed to withstand the frequent earthquakes that occur in this area, this 1,052-metre (3,451ft) cable-stayed structure has a central span of 320m (1,050ft) with 80m (263ft) of clearance and is supported by two 184-metre (604-foot) pylons.

Name	Bridge of the Americas
Location	Balboa, Panama
Crosses	Panama Canal
Type	Steel arch bridge
Function	Motorway bridge
Main span	344m (1,129ft)
Length	1,655m (5,430ft)
Clearance	106m (348ft)
Opened	1962
Design	Sverdrup & Parcel

MOVABLE BRIDGES

Bridges are often seen as immovable structures that use a variety of intelligent engineering methods to overcome local circumstances; for example, topography, shipping, natural forces such as heat, wind and potential disasters in the form of earthquakes or flood. However, sometimes it is the bridge itself that becomes an adaptable feature of the built environment; one of the smallest movable bridges can be found in Bermuda.

MOVEMENTS FOR SHIPPING
The swing bridges that were installed on the Panama Canal prior to the construction of the Bridge of the Americas are one of numerous types of movable bridges, designed to allow for the movement of shipping. These kinds of structures are pivoted and can be turned round into an open or closed position to allow vessels to pass through or for traffic to cross. Examples exist on waterways all over the world. Various other designs of moving bridges include transporter bridges (see page 142), folding bridges that are built in sections and telescope horizontally, and submersible bridges that can be lowered into the water.

THE SOMERSET DRAWBRIDGE
A drawbridge is hinged on one side and can be lifted. The principle originates as a defensive measure in the design of medieval castles and forts, where drawbridges could be lifted to prevent the moat being crossed. The same concept is used for bridges over water, except it is to allow passage beneath the bridge rather than to bar passage across it. Probably the world's smallest example is the Somerset Bridge in Bermuda, where a drawbridge connects Somerset Island with the mainland. It is just wide enough to allow for the mast of a yacht to pass through. An earlier bridge, dating from around 1620, was hand cranked to the open position, while the present-day structure comprises a pair of cantilevered half spans joined by a 45-centimetre (16 inch) wooden plank in the middle. When a boat needs to go through, the plank is removed by hand. One of the earliest examples of a drawbridge built to allow navigation to pass through was the medieval London Bridge, started in 1148, which had a drawbridge among its 20 spans.

MOVABLE TYPES AROUND THE WORLD
In the Netherlands, the traditional white wooden drawbridges are very much part of the waterway landscape. The best-known example is Magere Brug (the 'skinny bridge'), over the Amstel River, one of around 60 to be found in Amsterdam. Thought variously to have been named because of the narrowness of the original 1672 span or because of a story that it was erected by two skinny maidens as a short cut from their house, it was later rebuilt.

Among unusual variants on the drawbridge theme are two structures in Paddington Basin, on the Grand Union Canal in London. The 12-metre (39-foot) long Rolling Bridge (2004), made of eight hinged steel-and-wood sections was designed by Thomas Heatherwick. It retracts by being curled up into a tight octagon, when it looks more like a work of art than a bridge; its hydraulics are concealed within the handrail. By contrast, the glass-and-steel Helix Bridge retracts by rotating corkscrew-fashion.

BASCULE BRIDGES
Bascule bridges are also hinged, and additionally are counterbalanced by a weight. Tower Bridge (see page 134) is perhaps the most famous example,

Name	Somerset Bridge
Location	Bermuda
Connects	Somerset Island to the main isle
Type	Drawbridge
Function	Pedestrian bridge
Built	1620 (rebuilt since)

Right Reputedly the smallest drawbridge in the world, the Somerset Bridge in Bermuda allows the masts of sailboats to pass through a gap when a wooden board covering the centre span is removed.

although it is also part suspension bridge. The world's first large bascule bridge was the Nikolaevsky Bridge (later renamed Blagoveshchensky Bridge; rebuilt 2007) across the Neva in St Petersburg, Russia, in 1850; other bridges over the river have since also been built as bascule, and are raised each night. At Portland, Oregon, the Broadway Bridge is a unique double-leaf bascule span construction, 569m (1,867ft) long, and was the world's longest bascule bridge when completed in 1913.

Pegasus Bridge near Ouistreham in Normandy, France, is a 'rolling bascule' bridge that instead of pivoting moves by a rack and pinion mechanism. Originally called Bénouville Bridge, it was a key early triumph of the Allies during the Normandy Invasion in June 1944: its capture, along with other bridges, was the objective of Operation Tonga. It was replaced by a new rolling bascule bridge in 1994.

In 1996 Rotterdam acquired a major new landmark, the Erasmus Bridge across the Nieuwe Maas River. Designed by Ben van Berkel and completed in 1996 it is a highly distinctive amalgam of a bascule bridge with a cable-stayed structure. The larger cable-stayed portion has a asymmetrical 139 metre (456-foot) high asymmetrical pylon that has earned it the nickname of 'The Swan' while the southern span comprises a bascule bridge for ships that are too large to pass underneath.

Name	Erasmus Bridge
Location	Rotterdam, Netherlands
Crosses	Meuse River
Type	Bascule and cable-stayed
Function	Road bridge
Main span	280m (919ft)
Length	802m (2,631ft)
Opened	1996
Design	Ben van Berkel

Right Shortly after the Erasmus Bridge was opened to road traffic, it was noticed that the structure would swing under strong winds. Stronger shock dampers were installed to correct the movement.

Name	Rolling Bridge
Location	Paddington, London
Crosses	A dock close to the Grand Union Canal
Type	Curling/rolling bridge
Function	Pedestrian bridge
Opened	2004
Design	Thomas Heatherwick Studio

Right The Rolling Bridge, Paddington, is set in motion for passing boat traffic but remains a much more conventional bridge for the hundreds of people who cross it on foot each day.

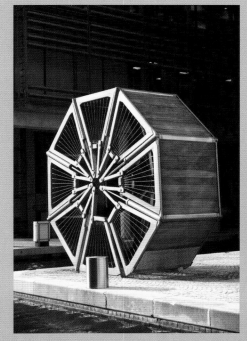

247

RIO-NITERÓI BRIDGE

GUANABARA BAY / **BRAZIL**

Carrying some 140,000 vehicles a day on a seemingly endless drive,
this snaking structure connects the city of Niterói with Brazil's capital
Rio de Janeiro using remarkably long central box girder spans,
including one which, at 300m (984ft), is the world's longest.

ROYAL OPENING
The idea of a crossing between Rio and
Niterói had been under discussion since
the 1870s. The alternatives were an hour's
ferry journey, or a 100-km (62.1-mile) round
trip by road. Eventually, following Brazil's
military coup of 1964, construction was
authorised by President Costa e Silva

Left Motorists who use the long and snaking dual
carriageway Rio-Niterói bridge only pay a toll when
heading away from Rio de Janeiro.

(president 1967–1969) and officially opened
during a state visit by Queen Elizabeth II
and the Duke of Edinburgh, in 1968. The
$22 million US, five-year project was in fact
an Anglo-Brazilian co-operation, financed
through British banks and carried out by
British firms. The bridge was officially
named after Costa e Silva.

AN OBJECT OF RESEARCH
Over the years the Rio-Niterói Bridge has
been the subject of several influential

technical experiments. One concerned
the innovative use of epoxy resin to glue
together precast segments of the concrete
superstructure, which has been proved not
to affect the safety of the bridge. Another
involved research into solutions for the
oscillations of the central spans that
were found to occur in relatively low-speed
cross winds and which had led to periodic
closures of the bridge. Various devices to
absorb the vibrations have been examined
including the use of dampers.

Name	Rio-Niterói Bridge
Location	Rio de Janeiro
Crosses	Guanabara Bay
Type	Reinforced concrete with steel box girder spans
Function	Road bridge
Span	300m (984ft)
Length	13.29km (8.2 miles), (8.8km (5.5 miles) over water)
Clearance	72m (236ft)
Opened	4 March 1974

ARACAJU-BARRA BRIDGE
This four-lane road bridge runs for 1.8 km (1.1 mile), with a cycle track
and pedestrian walkway alongside. Construction, by the Brazilian firm
EMSA, took just over two years. The two twin towers of the cable-stayed
bridge stand higher than the tallest building in Aracaju and are a major
landmark in the area, once a remote landscape of mangrove swamps.
This link between the regional capital of Aracaju, and the small town of
Barra dos Coqueiros was intended to boost tourism and economic
development, but has been the subject of much controversy.

Apart from budget wranglings, the bridge was involved in a naming
controversy. Officially, it was named after Joao Alves, the state governor,
who already had numerous public works projects named after him and
his family. Opponents argued that he had brought forward the bridge's
inauguration to September 2006 to boost his chances of re-election, they

sought to delay it, but succeeded only in obtaining an order preventing
Alves and his vice governor being present at the ceremony, and from
using any images of the bridge in their campaign. A preferred figure for
the name of the bridge is legendary local character Peixe ('Joe Fish'),
a master shipping pilot and lifeboatman responsible for saving many
lives in the treacherous tidal waters of the Sergipe. He was among the
first people to raise environmental concerns about sewage pollution
and the destruction of the native mangrove swamps around the city for
land reclamation schemes.

Right The Aracaju-Barra Bridge was designed by Mario De Miranda
of de Miranda Associates, Italy and was completed in just over two years
(between 2004 and 2006).

JUSCELINO KUBITSCHEK BRIDGE

BRASILIA / **BRAZIL**

The Juscelino Kubitschek (or simply JK) Bridge is named after the former Brazilian President who established the new and modern capital of Brasília in the late 1950s. Opened in 2002, it has rapidly become one of the city's most celebrated locations.

IN TUNE WITH THE CITY

The deck is supported by three steel arches, each set at an angle to the next – said to have been inspired by the playful image of a stone skipping over the surface of a lake. Architect Alexandre Chan says he considered numerous factors in his design, including the regional landscape, the architectural shapes already existing in the city, the position of the sunset and the need to give drivers a varying view.

The four massive concrete support blocks are submerged just a metre (3.3ft) below the lake surface, so that the arches appear to continue down into the water. Once temporary coffer dams had been lowered and pumped out where each support was to be created, some 4,000 cubic metres of concrete were poured for each support; 75cm (2.5ft) at a time with a three-day drying interval in between.

Each of the steel deck sections was assembled in a yard next to the site, raised and rolled into position onto temporary piers, then lowered by hydraulic jacks. The arches consisted of 83 sections, floated out and lifted into position by crane onto temporary arch supports. Finally, once

the cable stays had been attached, the temporary supports were removed to allow the arches to take the full weight of the decks. Fine adjustments were made to the cable tension assisted by remote-sensing from load cells installed in each upper anchor block. The cells convert a force into an electrical signal and continuously monitor the bridge's condition.

AESTHETIC MERIT

President Juscelino Kubitschek (1902–1976) is now seen as the father of modern Brazil. However, he received little immediate acclaim for his vision for Brasília, set as it was on a remote upland at the centre of the country. His deficit spending on such huge public works projects was blamed for setting off an inflationary spiral; Kubitschek lost office in 1961 and was deprived of his political rights after a military coup in 1964. Alexandre Chan's bridge, named in his honour, has been better received. In 2003 the project received the Gustav Lindenthal Medal, awarded at the annual International Bridge Conference, for a 'single, recent, outstanding achievement in bridge engineering, demonstrating technical and material innovation, aesthetic merit and harmony with the environment.'

Name	Juscelino Kubitschek Bridge
Location	Brasília
Crosses	Lake Paranoá
Type	Asymmetric arch bridge with suspended deck
Function	Road bridge
Span	Three 240-metre (787-ft) spans
Length	1,200m (3,937ft)
Height	60m (197ft)
Clearance	18m (59ft)
Opened	2002
Design	Alexandre Chan

Above Also known as the JK Bridge, the structure has become one of Brasilia's best-known landmarks. It crosses Lake Paranoá, a large artificial area of water on the eastern side of the city.

Right The deck of the bridge features six motorway lanes, three in each direction. It is also accessible to cyclists, skaters and walkers via a pedestrian walkway that runs alongside the main roadways.

INCA ROPE BRIDGES

HUINCHIRI / **PERU**

By the 16th century, the Inca civilisation of Peru had created some 200 highly advanced suspension bridges in plaited fibre, spanning gorges in the Andes mountains. Until the advent of iron and steel technology, the gorges remained uncrossable except by using traditional Inca structures such as this over the Apurimac Canyon.

COLONIAL WONDER

Spanish invaders, who began to arrive in 1532, were awe-struck by the bridges, some of which had planked floors, ropes as thick as a man's torso and filled-in sides so to prevent livestock from falling to their deaths. With spans of 45m (148ft) or more, they were longer than any European-style stone arch bridge spans of the time. Subsequently the colonists tried many times to erect stone arches over the gorges, but without success.

The Inca seem to have developed their suspension bridges without any outside influence, and were the only ancient American civilization to construct them. However, similar bridge-building techniques had developed independently in other mountainous parts of the world such as the Himalayas. In China iron chain suspension bridges date from the 3rd century BC.

A REGENERATING STRUCTURE

The greatest Inca rope bridges were found in the Apurimac Canyon along the main route north from the Inca capital of Cuzco. The most famous of these remained in service for about 450 years; it collapsed in the 1890s, inspiring Thornton Wilder's novel *The Bridge of San Luis Rey*.

Rope bridges sag over time, and were regularly rebuilt by local communities, their labour exacted as a form of tax. The last existing Inca suspension bridge, at Huinchiri on the Apurimac Canyon, is still ceremonially rebuilt each year in a three-day festival using techniques passed down in families since the Inca period. More than 15,000m (49,213ft) of grass cord is braided into the replacement ropes, and the four main cables, held apart by wooden cross-ties, have thick matting laid over them to provide a firm footing.

Right The weight of the combined materials used in rope bridges, such as that at Huinchiri, meant they tended to sag in the middle. However, they were very strong and could even support a person on horseback.

THE INCA TRUNK BRIDGE, MACHU PICCHU

Machu Picchu, an elaborate mountaintop citadel some 70km (43.5 miles) north west of Cuzco, was constructed at the height of Inca power around 1450. Only a century later, possibly depopulated by an epidemic, it lay largely abandoned and almost forgotten, and was never ransacked by Spanish invaders. A rope bridge provided a secret entrance, and could simply be burnt in the event of attack, while the Trunk Bridge was an ingenious defensive device protecting its western approaches. A six-metre (20ft) gap was left in the narrow trail cut into a sheer cliff, bridged by two tree trunks which could be removed if necessary to leave an impassable section with a 570-metre (1,870-foot) drop. Although fallen tree trunks must have formed been one of the earliest types of bridges, the effort and skill need to create this cliff-hugging stone path with its vertiginous gap would have required a great deal of technological and social organisation.

Right Without the tree trunk, the artifical gap purposefully created by the Inca would be impassable. Simple trunk bridges such as this were an effective means of defence against invaders.

Name	Keshwa Chaca (Q'eswachaka) Bridge
Location	Huinchiri, Peru
Crosses	River Apurimac
Type	Fibre rope suspension bridge
Function	Pedestrian bridge
Span	37m (121ft)
Clearance	24m (79ft)
Opened	Probably 15th century, reconstructed every one/two years

INDEX

255

ACKNOWLEDGEMENTS

The Automobile Association wishes to thank the following photographers, companies and picture libraries for their assistance in the preparation of this book.

Abbreviations for the picture credits are as follows – (t) top; (b) bottom; (l) left; (r) right; (c) centre; (AA) AA World Travel Library

2 © Jean-Philippe Arles/Reuters/Corbis; 8/9 Panoramic Images/Getty Images; 11 © Howard Kingsnorth/zefa/Corbis; 12t Joseph Baylor Roberts/National Geographic/Getty Images; 12b Chris Bland/Eye Ubiquitous/Corbis; 13t Photolibrary Group; 13b AA/M Chaplow; 14tl Philip Enticknap/Dorling Kindersley/Getty Images; 14tr © Gail Mooney/Corbis; 14bl © China Images/Alamy; 14br © Eye Ubiquitous/Hutchison; 15 AA/S Day; 16 Photolibrary Group; 17l © Franck Guiziou/Hemis/Corbis; 17r AA/M Jourdan; 18l AA/S McBride; 18r Photolibrary Group; 19 Photolibrary Group; 20 Photolibrary Group; 21l AA/C Coe; 21r AA/S Day; 22l AA/M Hayward; 22r Siegfried Layda/Stone/Getty Images; 23tl AA/A Lawson; 23tr AA/J Miller; 24l AA/C Lees; 24br Photolibrary Group; 25 © William S Kuta/Alamy; 26 Mary Evans Picture Library; 27l © Eye Ubiquitous/Hutchison; 27r © Philip Scalia/Alamy; 28l © Michael Dutton/Alamy; 28r © Anthony Collins/Alamy; 29 © Bob Krist/Corbis; 30tl © Atlantide Phototravel/Corbis; 30tr © Leslie Garland Picture Library/Alamy; 30bl Hulton Archive/Getty Images; 30br Hulton Archive/Getty Images; 31t AA/C Sawyer; 31b © Michael Maslan Historic Photographs/Corbis; 32 Hulton Archive/Getty Images; 33tl © Swim Ink 2, LLC/Corbis; 33tr © Alan Schein/Alamy; 34t © Corbis; 34b AA/J Smith; 35 Photolibrary Group; 36t © Frédéric Soltan/Sygma/Corbis; 36bl Photolibrary Group; 36br © Arco Images GmbH/Alamy; 37cr © ICP/Alamy; 37b Harlingue/Roger Viollet/Getty Images; 38l © Arcaid/Rex Features; 38cr Roger Viollet/Getty Images; 38br AA/K Paterson; 39tl AA/J A Tims; 39tr © Robert Holmes/Alamy; 39bl Photolibrary Group; 39br Scott Olson/Getty Images; 40tl © Fernando Alda/Corbis; 40tr © Eye Ubiquitous/Hutchison; 41t Pictures Colour Library; 41b © JTB Photo Communcations; 42/43 AA/A Mockford & N Bonetti; 44/45 Photolibrary Group; 46 Sipa Press/Rex Features; 47 © Otto Lang/Corbis; 48/49 AA/S McBride; 50/51 AA/S McBride; 51 AA/S McBride; 52 Photolibrary Group; 54/55 Sven Rosenhall/Nordic Photos/Getty Images; 56/57 Photolibrary Group; 57 AA/T Souter; 58/59 © Neil Emmerson/Robert Harding World Imagery/Corbis; 59 Photolibrary Group; 60/61 Pictures Colour Library; 62 © Joseph Sohm/Visions of America/Corbis; 62/63 © Jean-Pierre Lescourret/Corbis; 64/65 © Guenter Rossenbach/zefa/Corbis; 66t © Bruno de Hogues/Sygma/Corbis; 66b © Vince Streano/Corbis; 67 David Noble/Taxi/Getty Images; 68/69 Ethel Davies/Robert Harding World Imagery/Getty Images; 70/71 © Jean Roche/Grandeur Nature/Hoa-Qui/Imagestate; 71 AA/M Chaplow; 72/73 AA/A Baker; 74/75 Photolibrary Group; 76/77 © Luc Buerman/zefa/Corbis; 78t © Paul Thompson/Corbis; 78b AA/I Burgum; 79 Rolf Richardson/The Travel Library/Rex Features; 80/81 Photolibrary Group; 82 AA/C Jones; 82/83 Photolibrary Group; 84 AA/A Mockford & N Bonetti; 84/85 AA/A Mockford & N Bonetti; 86/87 AA/S McBride; 88c AA/C Sawyer; 88b © Werner Otto/Alamy; 89 AA/C Sawyer; 90/91 AA/M Wells; 92 AA/M Wells; 92/93 AA/M Wells; 94/95 Allan Baxter/The Image Bank/Getty Images; 96/97 © Fernando Alda/Corbis; 97 © William Zhang/Alamy;

98 AA/J Edmanson; 98/99 © Michael Nicholson/Corbis; 100/101 AA/P Wilson; 101 AA/M Chaplow; 102/103 © Bernie Epstein/Alamy; 104/105 © Ingemar Edfalk/Alamy; 106/107 AA/S Day; 108/109 © Images&Stories/Alamy; 110/111 © Paul Carstairs/Alamy; 111 © Ali Kabas/Alamy; 112/113 AA/G Edwardes; 114 Roy Garner/Rex Features; 114/115 AA/ G Edwardes; 116/117 AA/M Moody; 118t AA/M Moody; 118b Mary Evans Picture Library; 118/119 AA/M Moody; 120/121 AA/M Hayward; 122 AA/M Hayward; 122/123 AA/M Hayward; 124/125 AA/S Day; 126/127 AA/T Souter; 128/129 AA/N Jenkins; 130c Stringer/Hulton Archive/Getty Images; 130b Pictures Colour Library; 131 Kim Westerkov/Stone/Getty Images; 132 AA/R Moss; 133 britainonview/David Sellman; 134/135 AA/J A Tims; 136/137 AA/J A Tims; 138/139 AA/J Smith; 140/141 AA/J Smith; 141 Stringer/Hulton Archive/Getty Images; 142/143 © Jean Brooks/Alamy; 144l © Eryrie/Alamy; 144r Schutze+Rodemann/Bildarchive-Monheim/Arcaid; 145 © Rolf Richardson/Alamy; 146/147 AA/G Rowat; 148/149 Tony Howell/Photolibrary/Getty Images; 150/151 AA/R Coulam; 152 © Richard Klune/Corbis; 153 AA/R Coulam; 154/155 AA/J A Tims; 156 AA/N Setchfield; 156/157 AA/J A Tims; 158/159 © Imagebroker/Alamy; 160/161 Thierry Dosogne/Riser/Getty Images; 162 Cris Bouroncle/AFP/Getty Images; 163t Reuters/HO Old; 163c Cris Bouroncle/AFP/Getty Images; 164/165 Eye Ubiquitous; 166 Panoramic Images/Getty Images; 166/167 Larry Dale Gordon/The Image Bank/Getty Images; 168 Photolibrary Group; 170/171 © Eye Ubiquitous/Hutchison; 172 © Eye Ubiquitous/Hutchison; 173 Photolibrary Group; 174/175 Reuters/Stringer Shanghai; 176 Reuters/China Daily Information Corp – CDIC; 176/177 © Larry Leung/epa/Corbis; 178/179 AA/A Mockford & N Bonetti; 180/181 AA/A Mockford & N Bonetti; 182 © Neil McAllister; 184 Roger Viollet/Getty Images; 184/185 © Arthur Thévenart/Corbis; 186/187 © Murat Taner/zefa/Corbis; 188 © JTB Photo Communications, Inc/Alamy; 188/189 Nobuaki Sumida/Sebun Photo/Getty Images; 190/191 Photolibrary Group; 192t Pictures Colour Library; 192b AA/C Sawyer; 192/193 DAJ/Getty Images; 194 AA/M Langford; 196/197 Photolibrary Group; 198 AA/M Langford; 199 Photolibrary Group; 200 © Hulton-Deutsch Collection/Corbis; 201 Photolibrary Group; 202/203 AA/S Day; 204t FPG/Hulton Archive/Getty Images; 204b Photolibrary Group; 204/205 AA/P Kenward; 206/207 © David Pollack/Corbis; 208/209 Photolibrary Group; 210/211 © Andre Jenny/Alamy; 212/213 Fox Photos/Hulton Archive/Getty Images; 213 Keystone/Hulton Archive/Getty Images; 214/215 © Robert Estall/Corbis; 216 Lisa Romerein/Taxi/Getty Images; 216/217 Stephen St. John/National Geographic/Getty Images; 219 Photolibrary Group; 220 Lester Lefkowitz/The Image Bank/Getty Images; 221 Sipa Press/Rex Features; 222/223 Jerry Driendl/Stone/Getty Images; 224 AA/C Sawyer; 224/225 AA/C Sawyer; 226 Photolibrary Group; 227 © Bettmann/Corbis; 228/229 Richard T. Nowitz/National Geographic/Getty Images; 230 © Robert Holmes/Corbis; 232/233 AA/C Sawyer; 234/235 AA/C Sawyer; 235 Hulton Archive/Getty Images; 236 © Philip James Corwin/Corbis; 237 Pictures Colour Library; 238 Photolibrary Group; 240t Keystone/Hulton Archive/Getty Images; 240b Photolibrary Group; 240/241 Photolibrary Group; 242 © Pep Roig/Alamy; 244 Tom Fowlks/Stone/Getty Images; 244 Robert Harding World Imagery; 247t Murat Taner/Photographer's Choice/Getty Images; 247bl © Photofusion Picture Library/Alamy; 247br © Photofusion Picture Library/Alamy; 248 Eduardo Garcia/Photographer's Choice/Getty Images; 249 © SPP Images; 250 Cassio Vasconcellos/SambaPhoto/Getty Images; 251 Graca Seligman/SambaPhoto/Getty Images; 252 Peter Oxford/Nature Picture Library/Rex Features; 252/253 GlowImages/Getty Images

Every effort has been made to trace the copyright holders, and we apologise in advance for any unintentional omissions or errors. We would be pleased to apply any corrections in any following edition of this publication.